WOODWORKER BOOK OF WOOD… …ING

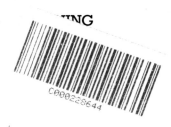

WOODWORKER BOOK OF WOOD-MACHINING

Argus Books

Argus Books Limited
1 Golden Square
London W1R 3AB

© Argus Books Ltd 1987

ISBN 0 85242 905 3

Phototypesetting by Rapidset & Design Ltd, London WC1
Printed and bound by Whitstable Litho

CONTENTS

ACKNOWLEDGEMENTS

The first and most important thank you by far must go to Gerry Baker of Luna Tools and Machinery, who invested a great deal of his company's time, space and money into the original production of the series. He lent the machines, the staff and the resources without which all those detailed photographs would just never have been possible. Almost more important, he immediately saw the value of the project, and supported it in spirit as well as with Luna's tangible resources. Luna Tools and Machinery are at 20 Denbigh Hall, Bletchley, Milton Keynes, Bucks MK3 7QT, tel. (0908) 70771.

Thank you also for much hard work to Judith Barker, who wrote the original text; to Derek Wales, who took all the photographs (except those in Chapter 9) with impressive efficiency, skill – and humour; and to Joe Wickens of Luna, who put a lot of effort into setting up the machines, making the jigs, and occasionally demonstrating. Many thanks also to Ken Taylor, who lectures at the London College of Furniture and for the Guild of Woodworkers, for checking the manuscripts, and to the staff of the Health and Safety Executive's Woodworking Industry National Group at Luton for their overall guidance.

Last but not least, thank you to Steven Hurrell, who wrote Chapter 9 on Dust extraction and wood waste removal.

INTRODUCTION

For centuries, men and women all over the world have been working in wood, either for enjoyment or to make a living. But never before has there been the same opportunity and incentive for Britain's woodworkers to combine business and pleasure. The twin demons of recession and unemployment, coupled with rapid technological development, have created a unique situation where many competent woodworkers, fearing or suffering from redundancy from their normal jobs, are deciding to put their skills to commercial use.

Those who are turning their hobby into a profession recognise the need for machinery. Today's woodworking machines do boring, repetitive jobs quickly and easily, allowing the woodworker time to concentrate his or her energy on the tasks which call for creative skill; more than that, they open up possibilities and potential for your work that simply don't exist when you do everything by hand.

The prospective purchaser of a machine can be overcome with confusion in the fast-growing market, which is why *Woodworker* provides its readers with regular updates on machinery. But far more important even than buying the right machine is knowing how to use it best.

This book is a revised, expanded, edited and updated version of the articles that appeared in *Woodworker* magazine between November 1985 and August 1986 under the title 'Machining Wood – Your expert guide'. The series was so popular, and, we felt, so useful, that the obvious step to take once it was over was to produce it as a book.

We have taken the opportunity to enlarge on technical points that for reasons of space and applicability were dealt with only in outline in the magazine series, but it remains to be said that the book, as the series, is an introduction to machining wood, not a comprehensive technical textbook. We have concentrated on the free-standing machines commonly found in the workshops of small professional, semi-professional, or serious amateur woodworkers; some readers will have only one or two of the machines featured, while many others will already be equipped at far higher levels of investment than the machinery featured here requires. Nevertheless, there is something here for everyone who loves wood and machinery and the way they come together; as a base for further experiment and accumulation of expertise, you could have no better. A particular strength of the Woodworker Book of Wood-Machining is its enormous number of photographs, which show exactly what you are doing, why and how as you stand over a machine.

Safety

Read Chapter 1 first. It is a guide to the Wood-

INTRODUCTION

working Machines Regulations 1974, which govern the use of woodworking machinery in professional and commercial workshops, and as you read the rest of the book we recommend that you constantly refer to it. You can get a copy of the Regulations from Her Majesty's Stationery Office in High Holborn, London WC2, if you wish to go into them in detail. Some of the photographs show practice that contravenes, in strict terms, the letter of the law; obviously we must show techniques for the non-professional, while in many cases clarity makes it necessary to remove guards. In any event, safety is the first and only golden rule; if you are unsure about a technique, the answer is quite simple – don't do it. Find another way round the problem. Many machines you can buy in this country also come with standard guarding and fences that conform only doubtfully with the Regulations; if you are unsure, check with your local Health and Safety Officer. You will soon realize that designing and making your own guards, fences and jigs is an early step on the path to creative, productive and enjoyable wood-machining.

The growth of enthusiasm for woodwork in all its myriad forms, the growth of the machinery market, and the growth of enforced or chosen leisure time make machinery a subject of ever-increasing interest to an ever-growing number of people. There is no doubt machines make much of the chore of woodwork disappear; but there is also the element of machining as a craft and an art in itself – and the machines as tools enjoyable to use in themselves – that makes the subject an attractive one. We hope you will enjoy this book, and we hope you will enjoy your machine woodwork all the more through it.

Aidan Walker
Editor, *Woodworker*

CHAPTER 1

SAFETY – THE FIRST PRIORITY

Statistics from the Health & Safety Executive show that some 90% of accidents at woodworking machines happen to the hands, and nearly one-third of them involve circular saws.

Although your hands are your first safety priority, don't under-estimate the value of your eyes and ears. Protect them whenever damage could be inflicted. Goggles or safety spectacles should *always* be worn while woodworking machines are in operation. You may be able to walk with a wooden leg, they say, but you can't see with a glass eye. Always wear ear protectors too when noise levels prevent normal conversation. Some machines are worse than others, planers generally taking first prize for decibels, so use your common sense.

Some safety rules apply to any machine in any workshop.

- Avoid using machinery when you're tired
- Never look or walk away from the machine when the blade and cutters are spinning, even after you've turned it off
- Always isolate the machine from the power supply when you are changing blades and cutters
- Always switch off when adjusting guards or fences
- Always take a firm stance at the machine, usually one foot forward and one back, and try to position yourself so you won't be in the way if bits and pieces fly
- Don't let rubbish accumulate on the floor round your feet
- Always wear neatly fitting overalls without loose or torn pockets, and put your wristwatch, rings, ties, flowing scarves and so on to one side; make sure that long hair is suitably secured to prevent it getting caught in moving mechanisms. Remember, 'moving' can mean anything from 4000 to 17,000rpm!
- More specifically, it is vital to reduce fire risks to a minimum. 'No smoking' is a rule which should always be respected
- Dust extraction should also be a major priority because, apart from the risks of lung damage, wood shavings and dust are highly combustible
- Fire prevention also depends on the highest standards of electrical safety. For example, powerful machines like the circular saw, planer and spindle/moulder, if they are on a single-phase supply, should always be wired directly into a 15amp fused mains outlet by a qualified electrician – a 13amp plug will not do.

Safety with woodworking machinery depends in the first instance on careful assembly and installation and, after that, on regular cleaning and maintenance according to the manufacturer's instructions. When you first install your machine, apart from checking it carefully you should read the instruction manual from cover to cover, going over the machine as you read so you know what is being explained.

Reliable manufacturers place great emphasis on safe operation of their machines, and many of them include safety checks in their manuals. Some firms provide customers with a spare-parts list as well as an instruction manual which explains assembly, operation methods, maintenance procedures, safety regulations, space requirements and trouble-shooting checks for each machine. Like all high-speed industrial equipment, woodworking machinery is subject to stringent safety regulations and should be supplied with suitable guards for your protection. It's up to you to use them.

But above all, safe wood-machining depends on the right mental attitude. A consistent, methodical approach will create and instil the good working practices on which safety in the workshop depends. Powerful machinery demands a healthy respect – but not fear. The wood-machinist must adopt an attitude finely balanced between confidence and caution. You need confidence to hold wood firmly and feed it smoothly through machining processes, and caution to avoid dubious short cuts.

The best short cut for woodworkers is to spend some time thinking and preparing before each machining task: working out exactly how the job can be done, whether you need jigs, the right settings on the machine, and the safety problems and their solutions.

One final safety requirement is to be sensitive to the sound and performance of individual machines when they are functioning correctly. Sparks and smoke are obvious signs that all is not well; the woodworker should also appreciate lesser evidence of malfunction. It is useful and cost-saving to have a certain level of mechanical knowledge, plus a basic tool kit which includes sockets, spanners, screwdrivers and Allen keys. Adjusting a drive belt, for example, is easily done, and can have a dramatic effect on machine performance.

The commercial workshop

Having made some introductory comments on machine safety, we should point out here that stringent regulations apply if you are engaged in woodworking '. . . by way of trade or for the purposes of gain', and carry on your business in a place that comes under the 1961 Factories Act. If it does, then it is also automatically subject to the Woodworking Machines Regulations 1974, and so are you. It is vital to understand your responsibilities here, especially with respect to your employees; the consequences of being found in contravention of these regulations should an accident occur could mean ruin. This is apart, of course, from the anguish of being the indirect cause of your own or someone else's serious – perhaps fatal – injury. Commercial woodworker or not, however, anyone with an aware and enthusiastic attitude will regard the Regulations as the best possible guide for setting up and working practices; they are not devised as hurdles to make your work and pastime more frustrating and expensive, they are written from the basis of the vast experience of the Factory Inspectorate in accident prevention and health protection. Amateur or professional, you should have a copy of the Regulations; they are available from Her Majesty's Stationery Office, 48 High Holborn, London WC1V 6HB. There is a range of related publications, all of which are available from HMSO. You can also get advice from the Health and Safety Executive, which has local offices throughout the country.

A brief introduction to the Woodworking Machines regulations 1974 is appropriate here – not a comprehensive guide, but a more detailed look, at least, at most of the operations described in the book in relation to the law and its main guarding premise, which is expressed in Regulation 5: 'Without prejudice to the other provisions of these regulations, the cutters of every woodworking machine shall be enclosed by a guard or guards to the greatest extent that is practicable having regard to the work being done thereat, unless the cutters are in such a position as to be safe to every person employed as they would be if so enclosed.'

The essence of this is that guarding should always be designed so it does not allow a hand to reach the cutter; the 'other provisions' mentioned include, for example, specific requirements for crown-guards at circular sawing machines and bridge-guards at overhand planers. The regulations list 12 basic machine types.

For verticle spindle moulders and high-speed routers there are specific requirements, laid down in Regulations 34 and 36; the first states that where it is impracticable to enclose the cutters so they are 'effectively guarded', but it is practicable to provide a jig or holder, the machine should not be used unless '. . . a jig or holder of such a design and so constructed as to hold firmly the material being machined and having suitable hand-holds which afford the operator a firm grip . . . is provided'. Regulation 36 covers eventualities in stopped work where jigs or holders that comply with Regulation 34 can't be used – it requires the provision of a suitable backstop.

The Woodworking Regulations 1974 also concern themselves fundamentally with training, allowing that there is a need to approach dangerous cutters only partially enclosed in a way that other industrial safety legislation would forbid, but insisting that operators of such machines must be trained to avoid danger. A familiar restriction in this area is the one on use of the more dangerous hand-fed machines by people under 18, but Regulation 13 also specifically requires that the operator/trainee has a knowledge of the safeguarding Regulations. This is the area in which the Health and Safety Inspectorate most often find woodworkers deficient – employers as well as employees. They just don't know what's illegal and what isn't.

Training in accordance with the Regulations isn't always easy to arrange, but machinery suppliers, Adult Education Institutes, Colleges of Further Education and some industry associations should all be able to offer either training or advice on where you can get it. You can also ask your local Health and Safety Executive office.

The accident picture

Though the figures for 1985 show a slight decrease in fatalities in the woodworking industry, it still remains more dangerous to work in it than down a mine. The H&SE is surveying the situation in detail, because accidents and injuries are not decreasing in relation to decreasing employment and a better safety record in comparable industries.

HM Inspectors' first 600 reports to be analysed show the majority of woodworking accidents occur at three basic machine types; 37% of the total at circular sawing machines, 23% at planers and thicknessers, and 16% at vertical spindle moulders and routers – 76% in all.

Those three are, of course, the machines most likely to be in small commercial workshops – larger industrial equipment is now often fully automated and fully enclosed. Remember also that if those figures were adjusted to take into account the relative numbers of the three machine types in use and the relative number of working hours spent at them, spindle moulders would very likely come out on top, and circular saws at the bottom of the table.

And we're not talking about broken legs or arms here, which will mend in time. Sometimes micro-surgery can stitch a cleanly severed finger – or even an arm – back on with some hope of regaining its use, but wood-machining injuries tend to be permanent. Not much chance of using your routed wrist or thicknessed hand again. It is difficult to quantify, but a single lost finger has been judged to equal 14% disablement. It's also healthy to bear in mind that experience doesn't immunise you; most people who use woodworking machines every day can tell you of someone they know or have heard of who had been working for years and only recently got caught in a planer or spindle moulder.

Machine by machine

Circular saws

Riving knives – the plate that stands behind the blade to prevent the wood closing in on the blade as it cuts, trapping and kicking back – should be kept adjusted as close as practicable to the blade. They should be the right thickness, that is slightly thicker than the plate of a blade but fractionally thinner than the kerf, or saw-cut. Crown-guards, the cover over the top of the blade, should extend from the top of the riving knife to a point as close as possible to the surface of the timber you are cutting. Both these requirements mean that crown-guards mounted on the riving knife itself are often unsatisfactory – flimsy and awkward – and you should look carefully at these guarding arrangements when you are buying a machine. You should never be able to get your hand to a circular saw-blade as it is cutting, because the gap between crown-guard and material should not be big enough. It's not necessary to 'see the cut' if the machine and its fence is set up right.

Ripping – cutting along the grain – can put a lot of strain on motor and blade, and the regulations prohibit ripping where the teeth of the blade do not project above the surface of the workpiece all along its length.

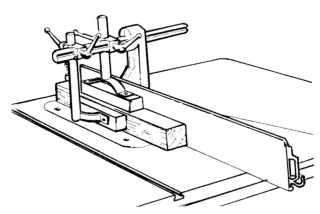

Fig. 1.1: Rebating, grooving and similar work on a circular saw must be guarded with Shaw-type pressure-pads or tunnel-guards like the one at right

Rebating, tenoning, moulding and grooving on a circular saw are illegal when the blade is not effectively guarded. If you use a proprietary tenoning jig such as the one illustrated in fig. 2.27, you should use it with guards like the ones in figs 1.1 and 1.2. If these operations involve breaking into or out of the timber, the law says you must not do it, irrespective of the depth of cut.

Narrow bandsaws

Friction discs or rollers must be adjusted as close as possible to the table, taking into account the work you are doing. The length of blade that runs between the guides and rollers and the top wheel must be guarded by a flanged front plate (see Chapter 4, the Bandsaw).

Spindle moulders

Cutters should be the right ones for the blocks you are using (see Chapter 6, the Spindle moulder). Block design has improved tremendously recently with regard to safety – many manufacturers have introduced positive location features like wedge-shaped inserts and pins, with corresponding grooves or slots in the cutters – but always remember there is an ever-present danger of cutters flying out. People have died at the spindle moulder. The manufacturer's instructions on peripheral speed and cutter projection should be strictly adhered to.

Cutter-guards must be made strong enough to hold in flying cutters or parts. Home-made guards abound in spindle moulding, but they must be of really substantial ply or timber. All timber guards and false fences must be good and strong, and they should all be secured in place while you test the set-up as well as while you work.

Straight work on the spindle moulder should present no guarding problems when the cut is the full length of the workpiece. Standard equipment supplied with the machines – especially ones imported from countries with different regulations – can often allow your hand to touch the cutter if the wood kicks back. You can extend Shaw-type guards (figs 1.3 and 1.4) to enclose the cutters properly.

Face boards and/or false fences (see Chapter 6) must be used, says the law, to reduce the gap between straight fences as far as possible. They enclose cutters, and give vital support to the workpiece when it is at the cutters, just where it is most needed (fig. 1.5). Chapter 6 explains how to fit these fences – you need to break the spinning cutter through it after it has been fixed

– but better machines have screw adjustments for their standard fences to which the false fences are attached, which means the breakthrough operation can be done comparatively safely.

Jigs or holders should be used, with proper hand-holds, whenever effective guarding is not practicable – as for instance in circular or shaped work (fig. 1.6).

Stopped work is particularly dangerous because

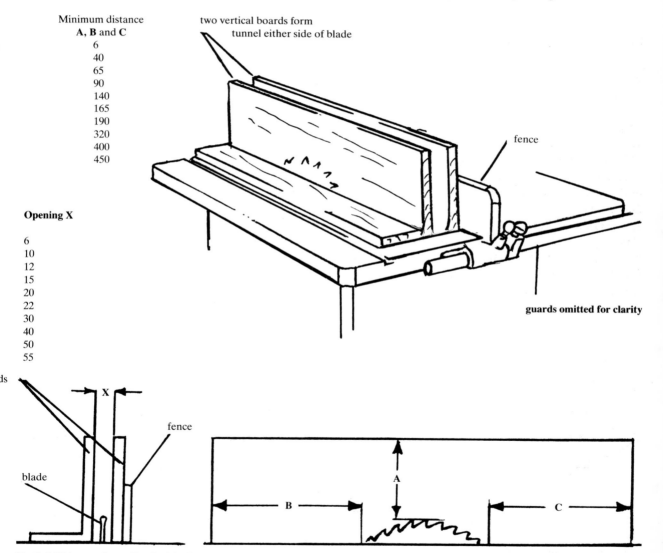

Minimum distance
A, B and **C**
6
40
65
90
140
165
190
320
400
450

Opening X

6
10
12
15
20
22
30
40
50
55

two vertical boards form
tunnel either side of blade

fence

guards omitted for clarity

X

fence

blade

A

B

C

Fig. 1.2: This sort of guarding for jobs like rebating and grooving must only be used when the work is high enough to be *firmly held* above the vertical boards

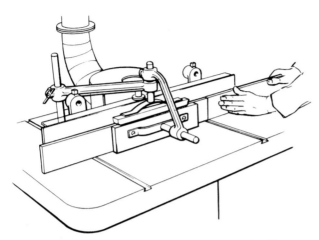

Fig. 1.3: Straight work on the spindle moulder, using Shaw guards with two pressure-pads

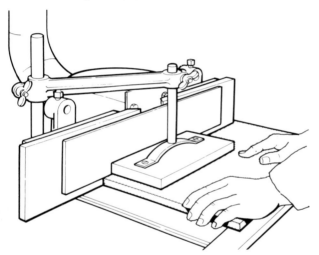

Fig. 1.4: Wide flat work on the spindle moulder may only need one pressure-pad with the Shaw guard

of the likelihood of kick-back, against which the law requires a backstop, and preferably a jig or holder as well. Back and front stops are best, and usually quite easy to fix, especially with a false table such as the one in fig. 1.7.

Mortisers

Mortisers are comparatively safe – the commonest hand-operated hollow-chisel type, at least. Chain mortisers, however, require enclosure of the parts of the chain not buried in the timber,

and horizontal slot-mortisers, very common on the popular universal machines, can be used with a false fence that encloses as much of the cutter as possible. The heavier industrial swinging-chisel or reciprocating mortisers require cutter enclosure, which usually has to be designed and made for the job in hand.

Planers and thicknessers

Surfacing and edging (see Chapter 3) without resetting the bridge guard between the alternate operations is permitted, says Regulation 27, as long as there is no more than 10mm clearance under the guard and from its end to the flat face of the work. A very common accident is the one wherein a hand drops from the back end of the workpiece on to the cutters between bridge-guard and fence.

Chamfering is safer using a second fence or guide clamped to the infeed table to stop the work sliding 'down the hill' under the bridge-guard.

Recessing, rebating, tenoning and moulding on planers are illegal unless either the cutters are effectively guarded or you are using an attachment which has been given a Certificate of Exemption. This usually means you must have a sliding carriage arrangement.

Planer/thicknessers – dual purpose machines – must have complete guarding for the cutters above the table when they are being used for thicknessing. An extraction duct (see chapter 9), if it is strong enough, usually complies. There must also be a 'nip bar' to stop fingers being trapped between the feed rollers and the timber. You must only feed pieces one at a time into any sort of thicknesser if it does not have divided feed rollers or anti-kickback fingers.

Wood waste and sanding

Chip removal The law clearly states that thicknessers and spindle moulders (when the latter are used more than six hours a week) must have effective extraction. High-speed routers, difficult to extract, can be used with some means of

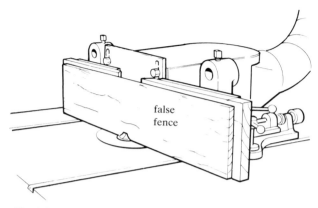

Fig. 1.5: Use a false fence wherever you can to reduce exposure of the cutters

Workshop fires which have no identifiable cause at all are horrifyingly common – they just start in all the old rubbish that so many people allow to accumulate. Fire hazards should never be underestimated, especially if you work alone.

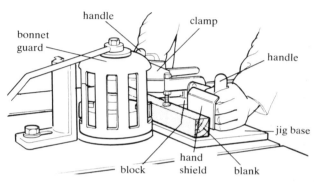

Fig. 1.6: Make sure your jigs have good hand-guards and workpiece-holding clamps

blowing away chips rather than sucking them. This isn't just good practice, it's the law.

Dust and health
Cancer research has led to the permitted limits of exposure to dust in commercial concerns being lowered recently. Bear this in mind when you are fixing up your extraction, especially if you use a lot of hardwoods; the enthusiastic amateur, too, is not immune to nasal cancer!

Fire and explosion
Fine sanding dust – particles of less than 500m, or less than 5/1000mm, is explosible, and if more than 10% of the total volume that goes into your extraction system is made up of this dust, you should beware. Board materials like medium-density fibreboard can also produce dust particles of this size from cutting as well as sanding operations, so don't just look at the sanding part of it.

Explosible waste should go into a collector outside the workshop, carefully designed and in a safe place. Small extraction collectors inside the workshop need a protective enclosure, and this is really a matter for ventilation experts. Get advice from the Health and Safety office. If you use wood-burning stoves to heat your work area, don't feed them with flammable dust, which can flash back.

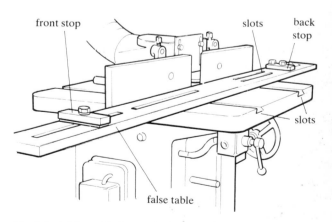

Fig. 1.7: A false table for a spindle moulder should have dovetail battens underneath to locate in the table-slots. Stops adjustable; guards not shown

Publications

The British Standard Code of Practice on the Safeguarding of Woodworking Machines should be published in 1987. It is divided into sections – a general one plus specific information on circular saws, spindle moulders, high-speed routers including hand-held machines, shapers and CNC equipment, planers and thicknessers, and narrow bandsaws.

The Woodworking Machines Regulations 1974 – Statutory Instrument 1974, no.903
Safety in the Use of Woodworking Machines, Guidance Note PM21

Guards for Planing Machines, Guidance Note PM2
Safety in the Use of Woodworking Machines, HSW Booklet no. 41
Furniture and Woodworking, Health and Safety 1977
A Guide to the Woodworking Machines Regulations 1974, Health and Safety Series Booklet HS (R) 9

All the above are available from HM Stationery Office or Government Bookshops. There is also *Wood Dust: Hazards and Precautions – A Guide for Employers*: a leaflet available free from local offices of the Health and Safety Executive.

CHAPTER 2

THE CIRCULAR SAW

No one ever got very far in woodwork without sawing a straight cut. The priority in any workshop must be the circular saw, which makes light work of straight-line sawing and at the same time is versatile enough to accomplish a number of intricate and demanding tasks with great precision.

Blades

It pays to start with a good basic understanding of the way different saw-blades work, why there are different designs, and how differently they all do the same job. There are five main groups of saw-blade (figs 2.1, 2.2):
• Ripsaws, for cutting along the grain and severing wood fibres edge from edge, have teeth with tops like chisel edges, inclined compara-

Fig. 2.1: All tungsten-carbide-tipped ripping blades, except the HSS 10in (top left) and ultra-fine 96-tooth 12in panel blade (bottom right). The fewer the teeth, the coarser the finish

tively far forward ('positive hook'), and no cutting bevel on their front edges. As a ripsaw moves through the wood, it takes away chip after chip, tooth after tooth, (fig. 2.3), cutting the fibres cleanly at the side. The teeth have strong 'back-up' – a feature of the positive hook – and there are generally fewer points per inch than with crosscut teeth, because the wood removed in the 'kerf' – the width of cut – tends more to hold together than with crosscutting, and clearance is needed for the waste. Ripsaw teeth cut a 'front slice' (fig. 2.2).

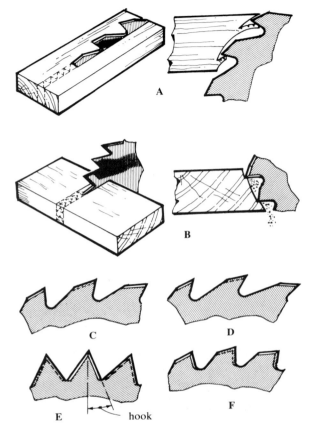

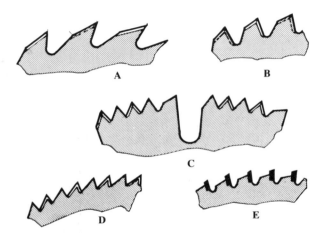

Fig. 2.2: Types of saw teeth. A, ripsaw teeth with positive hook; B, crosscut teeth with 'negative hook'. C, a dimension blade with both rip and crosscut teeth; D, small fine teeth for manufactured board, and E a TCT panel blade

Fig. 2.3: A, ripsaw teeth remove the wood chip by chip; B, cross-cutting teeth have a 'side-slice' action. C, hardwood rip teeth with a small hook angle, D, softwood rip teeth with a bigger one; E, softwood crosscut teeth with large negative hook angle, F hardwood crosscut teeth with smaller negative hook and strong back-up

● Crosscut saws cut across the grain, actually slicing through the fibres rather than separating them. For this reason crosscut teeth must chop either side of the blade (fig. 2.3), so they are arranged with more 'set' than ripsaws, alternate teeth pushing out to alternate sides very slightly; they have sharp points and 'negative hook' – ie, the teeth incline back from a radial line from the centre of the blade – with usually a front bevel to the teeth as well for a side-slicing, clean cut. Cutting across the grain can cause 'spelching', or whiskering of the fibres on the underside of the board where the blade exists (fig. 2.4), which is minimised by the teeth trailing into the fibres

Fig. 2.4: Spelching on the right

THE CIRCULAR SAW

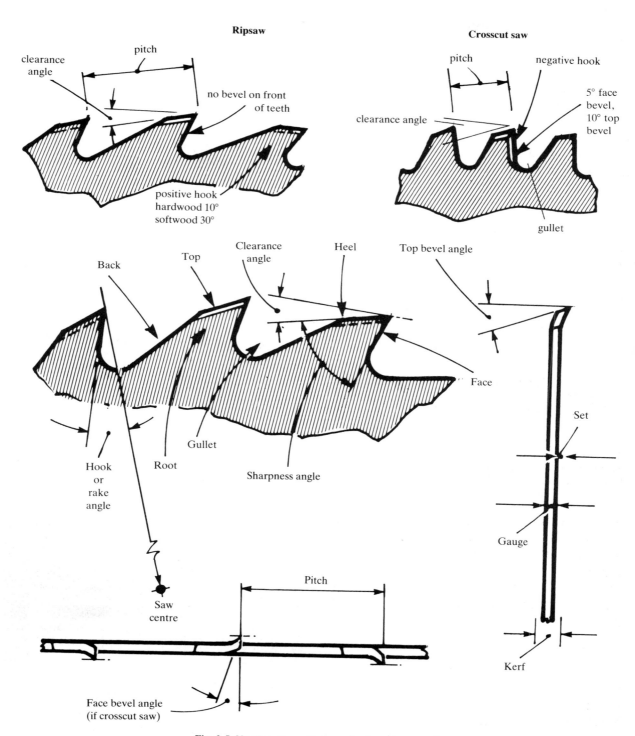

Ripsaw

clearance angle

pitch

no bevel on front of teeth

positive hook hardwood 10° softwood 30°

Crosscut saw

pitch

negative hook

5° face bevel, 10° top bevel

clearance angle

gullet

Back

Top

Clearance angle

Heel

Top bevel angle

Face

Hook or rake angle

Root

Gullet

Sharpness angle

Saw centre

Set

Gauge

Kerf

Pitch

Face bevel angle (if crosscut saw)

Fig. 2.5: Naming of saw-blade parts plus average angles

rather than leaning forward into them. Just crosscut a board with a ripsaw blade and you will see how much 'spelching' occurs. There is also a difference in tooth design for hardwoods and softwoods: hardwood ripteeth have less positive hook than softwoods – the material is more brittle – and hardwood crosscut teeth are arranged with less negative hook than their softwood counterparts, for the same reason. They have more metal behind the tooth, however, for greater strength. 'Naming of parts' for saw-blades and their basic geometry are shown in fig. 2.5.

- Dimension saws cut wood at any angle, across or along the grain, and so need a combination of rip and crosscut teeth, with good big gullets between the teeth for waste clearance. These blades can also be known as 'general purpose' blades because they carry both kinds of teeth, but the same name can also apply to blades with a rather unsatisfactory compromise of tooth shape between rip and crosscut. GP saws are not as popular as they were, with good reason; dimension saws are more common in industry where a lot of panel cutting in solid wood might be done exclusively by one machine.

- Fine saws or panel saws, for plywood and laminated manufactured board, have more teeth per inch than any other, to minimise the whiskering that is almost inevitable with materials made up of thin veneers. The more teeth per inch, the finer the cut and the less the spelch.

- Abrasive blades are specifically for cutting materials with a high content of hard glues or bonding agents which would blunt normal carbon-steel teeth in no time at all. Don't even attempt, for instance, to cut plastic laminate or perspex with anything other than tungsten carbide. In fact, the amazing hardness of tungsten-carbide teeth, which can stay sharp for as much as ten times longer than ordinary carbon-steel teeth, has meant that they are now very popular for almost all sawing jobs. Rip, crosscut, GP and dimension teeth can be and are all made of tungsten carbide, and their higher cost is well repaid in length of time between sharpening. They are,

however, brittle, and can chip or fly off if they are worked blunt or hit nails and other enemies. You cannot generally, of course, sharpen TCT (tungsten-carbide tipped) teeth with your own file, but it isn't advisable anyway to try this beyond a bit of 'dressing' with ordinary saw-blades unless you are a real expert. There are some jobs where TCT teeth will not be desirable – for fine cutting in thin solid-wood panels, carbon steel usually gives a finer finish to the cut. This is for the connoisseurs.

Most of the blades you will come across are plate saws, the faces of which are parallel in thickness. The set of the teeth allows the thickness of the blade to travel freely in the kerf. TCT saws don't generally have set as such, because the tips themselves are thicker than the plate on to which they are brazed, and that in itself gives clearance for the blade in the kerf. Hollow-ground blades also have that effect – the body or 'web' of the blade is ground thinner than the teeth and the centre – but they are for specialised dimension work, and can leave a very fine 'planed' finish to the cut. There are other types of thin rim saw-blade – swage, taper and ground off – all of which are designed to minimise waste. Their applications are limited and specialised; you shouldn't need to bother about these unless you are production manager of a very large woodworking plant!

Maintenance

It is a golden rule of all wood-machining that blunt cutters do damage to the work and the machine. Your ears will become attuned to the sound of a sharp or blunt blade, and you will feel the machine having to work harder and take greater strain on the bearings. Economising on changeover and sharpening time is no economy at all; the results of laziness in this area, or refusing to change a blade because of pressure of time, can be very expensive indeed. Saw-blades also need to be kept in perfect dynamic balance and correct tension, and the teeth need to form a perfect cutting circle. A good saw doctor will look after all these things for you, although it pays to know enough about your blades to be able to dress ordinary teeth occasionally – hold a fine file stationary and turn the blade tooth by tooth against it by hand, with the power isolated at the mains. Sympathy to the sound and feel of the work that blade and machine are doing pays dividends.

Control of the cut

The other area of cutting theory with which you should have at least a passing acquaintance is the one of peripheral speeds and feed speed. There is an optimum 'peripheral' cutting speed for every saw-blade, where it is working most efficiently; blade size and motor rpm obviously govern this directly, but you can also slow a saw-blade down by pushing the work into it too quickly. The motor is strained as well; the cut becomes harsh, the waste cannot clear, and the finish is rough and can even burn.

Imagine jamming a piece of wood up against a saw-blade and then turning the motor on; it wouldn't turn or cut, of course. This is why you must let the machine get the blade to its free-running speed before you feed the work into it. Try and keep the blade speed as near its free-running rate as you can while you cut, and you will be getting optimum results. You will also reduce peripheral speed and thus efficiency if you use saw-blades smaller than the ones for which the machine is designed; smaller circumference means, of course, smaller peripheral speed. Don't go less than six tenths of the diameter of the blade that came with the saw.

Chip thickness means the amount of single 'bite' a cutter or saw tooth removes as it passes once through the work. It is decided by the projection of a tooth from its neighbours at the point where it is taking maximum depth in the work. Modern blade designs often now include built-in chip limiters (fig. 2.6), so you can't damage the blade or work by setting it too deep and

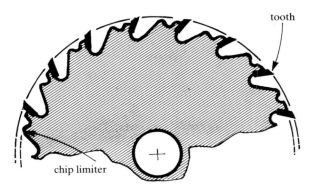

Fig. 2.6: Saws with widely spaced teeth often have chip-limiters in front of each tip to reduce the chance of kick-back

feeding it too quickly; if you do feed too fast, the work will meet the blunt limiters before it meets the teeth, and the wood will ride up on the blade – a potentially very dangerous situation. This can happen all too easily with blades without limiters as well; it is also a result of blunt teeth, or worse still, a blade mounted the wrong way in the machine. It can happen!

Machine techniques

Ripping
Ripsawing can be unexpectedly dangerous. Look at the wood. The danger is that the saw

Fig. 2.7: A circular sawbench has to be the first machine you go for if you're serious about your workshop; get the biggest blade-size and most powerful motor you can afford. Note the dust extraction outlet and sliding crosscut table

will snatch and toss the wood back at your stomach – at about 100mph. When ripping bowed material, always place the rounded (convex) side against the rip-fence to prevent chattering and possible throwback. The action of the saw keeps the wood down on the table; but look at the grain as well as the shape of the piece. If the grain is unduly wild, the workpiece might lift and make the cut difficult to control; have two pushsticks (figs 2.8, 2.9), one to hold it down, the other to push the last 12in past the blade.

Apart from looking at the grain, make a note of splits or knots. If the cut goes across a split diagonally, you might find the blade cutting a wedge, catching it, and throwing it back and up – to about eye height. For that reason if no other. . .

Take the correct stance. Apart from standing to one side of the saw-blade and the workpiece, you should also be in a good position to feed the wood firmly and smoothly into the machine (fig 2.10), ideally with the left foot forward and the

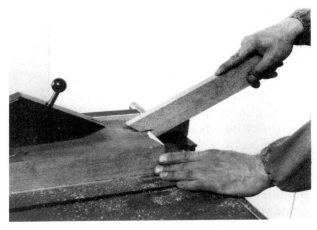

Fig. 2.9: Always have the push-stick just to hand before you start to cut, and always use it for the last 12in. Sometimes you'll need two sticks. The angle of the notch is important for positive location on the workpiece

left hand (well back from the blade) holding the wood against the rip-fence while the right hand pushes the workpiece towards the saw-blade. Always have your push-sticks to hand – you can't leave a piece of wood half-cut with the

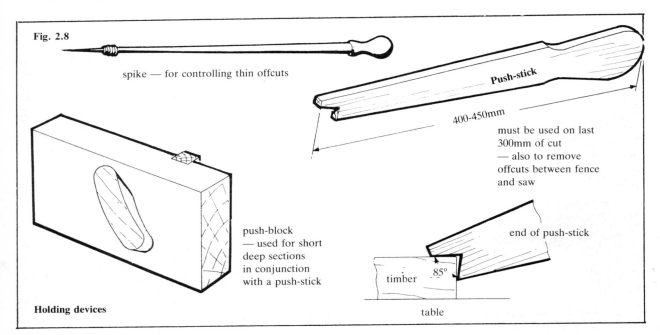

Fig. 2.8

spike — for controlling thin offcuts

Push-stick

400-450mm

must be used on last 300mm of cut — also to remove offcuts between fence and saw

push-block — used for short deep sections in conjunction with a push-stick

end of push-stick

timber   85°

table

Holding devices

blade spinning while you walk over to the bench and pick them up!

Set the machine carefully and use all the guards. Setting the machine presents a classic case for the methodical approach. Mentally number each adjustment; and, when they have all been made, check them again by number to ensure that everything is *securely* in the right place. Let someone else answer the telephone while you concentrate on the setting procedure – a distraction could be costly and harmful.

Blade height is important (fig 2.11). The saw-blade should be set so that the gullet of the teeth (the maximum depth between them) is level with the top of the wood to be cut. This ensures that the maximum number of teeth are working through the wood, reducing surface friction and

Fig. 2.10: The right stance for ripping; keep your body out of line with the back of the blade as much as you can. The left hand presses the timber in to the fence; the push-stick is at the ready (though out of sight here) to deal with the last 12in of the cut

Fig. 2.11: The handle in the foreground adjusts blade height and angle. On some saws the calibrations on the rip-fence (shown here without an auxiliary fence) can be adjusted – you can just see the screw to allow movement of the pointer against the scale

consequent heating of the saw-blade, plus its tendency to snatch. At least one tooth should be in contact with the material at any moment, to regulate the rate of hand feed. A small pitch – the distance between tooth points – is essential for thin material, so that it is not fed too far forward into the gullet before the next tooth cuts; this prevents snatching.

The riving-knife (fig. 2.12) is a vital safety feature of the circular saw, especially when ripping, since it acts as a wedge and prevents the saw-cut from closing behind the blade. This stops the wood kicking back at you. The riving-knife should be set as close to the saw-blade as possible – not more than 25mm below its highest point, and not more than 12mm away from the back of the blade.

When you're ripping long, wide, boards, the riving-knife will not stop the cut closing and possibly jamming, so you might need wedges placed in the cut; obviously you need someone else at the other end for this. In any case, the riving-knife must always be two gauges thicker than the blade, but thinner, of course, than the kerf.

The top guard (fig. 2.13) should be set as close to the wood as possible, and never more than 12mm above it. This guard prevents the wood from lifting up if it snatches, and covers the maximum amount of saw-blade to reduce the risk of injury. You should not be able to get your fingers between it and the work.

The fences

The two basic surfaces, the table and the rip-fence (fig. 2.11), must be true and correctly set. A first-class straight-edge will tell you whether the table surface is true. Inspect the alignment of the rip-fence and the saw-blade – they should be fractionally out of parallel; some say 'toe out',

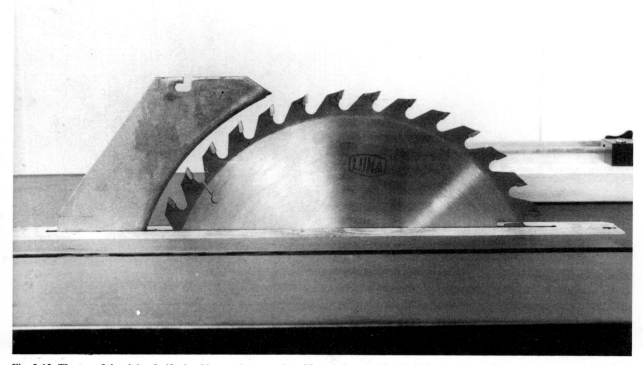

Fig. 2.12: The top of the riving-knife should never be more than 25mm below the blade's highest point, and the curve as near to the blade as possible. It should be marginally thinner than the kerf, but thicker than the plate of a blade

Fig. 2.13: Top-guard adjustments vary from saw to saw; does the tightening knob maddeningly crank up to a position where it fouls the wood? 'No higher than 12mm above the work' is the rule for guards. You can see the auxiliary fence behind the blade

something like $1/32$ in in 5ft further apart at the back of the table, some say 'toe in' to bring the fence closer to the back of the blade and keep the work under control. In any case the amounts are microscopic; just don't have the machine set up so the work either binds or wanders.

When you're setting up a cut, be very fussy about getting the rip-fence right. Remember to measure the cutting width, depending on which side of the saw-blade you are working. Don't forget that the blade will remove 3 or 4mm of the wood – so make sure it won't be removed from the piece you are measuring. Some saws have fine adjusters on the faces for accurate setting (fig. 2.11), the calibration should be adjustable, too. The rip-fence will slide back and forth; for

'coarse' ripping (of unplaned timber) the forward edge should line up with the gullets on the front of the blade. Ripping panels needs the fence further forward.

Rip-fences are generally supplied with holes which enable you to bolt or screw to them a variety of auxiliary or false fences (fig. 2.14) when safety and/or the job calls for them. You will find yourself making various shapes and sizes of auxiliary fences and guards for specific tasks.

The auxiliary fence is particularly useful when crosscutting or ripping small pieces of wood and when cutting thin strips and veneers. Small pieces of wood are inclined to jam between blade and fence, so the auxiliary fence should be set to allow the cut pieces to move away from the blade after cutting.

Fig. 2.14: The auxiliary fence is essential if you are cutting thin strips off a wide piece, to stop them jamming between blade and fence. You should have a number of extra fences for various jobs, each designed for versatility, strength and safety

Other points

When ripping very long or very wide boards, you will need the help of an assistant, an adjustable roller stand (fig. 2.15) or both. You can buy roller stands, some with a choice of 'roll-along' or 'roll-across'; stands can also be made in the workshop, adjustable with butterfly nuts. Whichever type you use, the stand should be adjusted so that it is slightly below the level of the saw-table, since the wood falls a little as it comes off the saw, and it's important that it

Fig. 2.15: Set your roller stand (bought or home-made) according to the length you're cutting. The wood should drop on to the stand ever so slightly, so you avoid embarrassing and dangerous push-overs

shouldn't catch on the stand as it is fed through the machine.

Don't forget to wear goggles or safety spectacles to protect your eyes, and also attach the saw to a dust-extraction facility. Don't despair if you can't afford a proprietary one – vacuum-cleaners work very well on small machines. See Chapter 9 for more details on this.

Keep watching the saw-blade until it stops moving. Some machines have a brake on the motor to stop the saw quickly, a design feature required by safety regulations in other countries. Most new equipment available in Britain incorporates the brake as standard.

For getting a good straight edge on bent, warped or curved boards, or 'waney edged' planks (with the irregular bark still on the edges), you need a method of passing the work over the blade that does not need the datum surface of fence or table. The straight-edging jig (fig. 2.16) is the answer to this problem; cut a strip of thick ply or blockboard as long as you can get, fix a stout stop batten at one end, and a hardwood strip underneath that fits the grooves in your saw-table. You can then slide the under-batten in the groove and clamp the board to be cut on the jig – or put panel pins through it from the underside so their points just show, which will hold the board so it doesn't move about as you cut. Line your board up on the jig so the blade will make an unbroken cut – minimum waste, obviously – set the blade running, and pass jig and board past the blade. Now you have one good straight edge.

Crosscutting

A crosscut fence is the single most important addition to any table-saw. Most decent machines will come with at least some sort of crosscutting arrangement; the simplest, cheapest and least accurate is the 'mitre guide', which slides in the table grooves, to give you an accurate 90° crosscut if you set it at 90° and hold it hard to the workpiece while you pass that past the blade.

THE CIRCULAR SAW

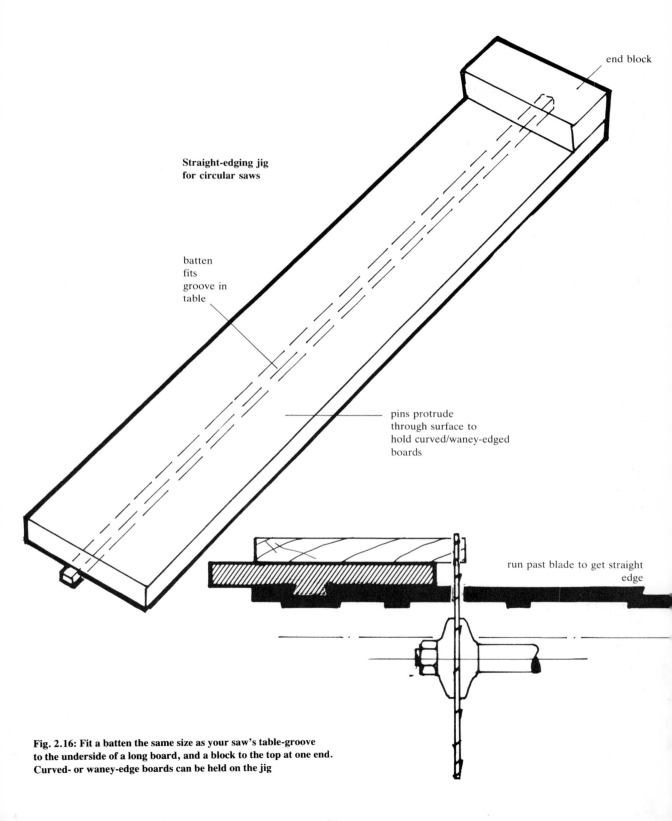

end block

**Straight-edging jig
for circular saws**

batten
fits
groove in
table

pins protrude
through surface to
hold curved/waney-edged
boards

run past blade to get straight
edge

**Fig. 2.16: Fit a batten the same size as your saw's table-groove
to the underside of a long board, and a block to the top at one end.
Curved- or waney-edge boards can be held on the jig**

These are usually fiddly, light and too small for much of the work you will want to do. There are fences which run on bars and carriages at the side of the table, like the one in Fig. 2.17; there

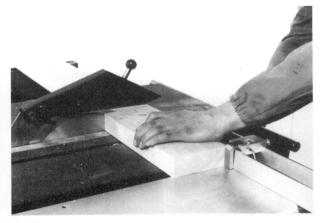

Fig. 2.17: The surface of the sliding table and one of the crosscut stops can be seen in the foreground; a firm grip holds the work back to the fence

are even complete sliding tables, and on the very expensive dimension or panel saws the greater part of the whole structure is an 8ft table (at least) sliding on a 12ft – or longer – track. Whatever the price or capacity of the crosscut fence or table, it is never right to assume that it will cut a perfect 90° without careful adjustment and constant checking and maintenance. The good designs will be comparatively easy to adjust. Most machines come with some form of marked-on calibration, but in their very nature these are unlikely to be perfectly accurate, so it always pays to make a few cuts, check what you are getting, and adjust. The crosscut table or fence should also be perfectly parallel with the flat surface of the saw-table, and there will be height adjustment on the good ones as well.

There are some crosscutting operations which require the rip-fence, usually with the auxiliary fence as well, to be set up; but in most cases you will not need the rip-fence while you are crosscutting, which means you should check how easily you can get the rip-fence out of the way. Does it slide up and down the back bar easily (fig. 2.11), or is it a pain to move?

Assume that the end of a bought board is never perfectly square – it will need trimming, and the accuracy of the 90° setting of the crosscut fence will need to be checked. There are two methods of doing this:

● Make two face-marks and two edge-marks on an established straight edge of your board so there'll be one each side of the blade when you make the cut. Turn both pieces over to get the datum straight edge of the board against the crosscut fence and trim the cut ends of each. Then put the two cut ends together, face- and edge-marks in line on a perfectly flat surface like the saw-table (fig. 2.18). Any error in the setting will be doubled and will show up as the cut ends are placed together. You can then adjust the setting of the crosscut fence, remembering that if the error is doubled you must adjust half that value.

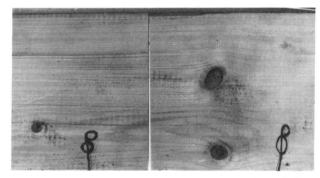

Fig. 2.18: With two face and edge marks, you can set the good edge flat and see where the error is. A doubled fault is easier to see – but remember to adjust your fences half the value of the error

● A simpler but less accurate method is to make a cut, turn one piece over and place the cut ends together on a reliably flat surface. Again, the error – if any – will be obvious; but bear in mind that you have not used one side only of the board as a datum against the crosscut fence, and the edges may not be parallel anyway.

Repeat cutting of short pieces of the same length from a board (fig. 2.19) is one crosscutting operation where the rip-fence can be used in conjunction with the crosscut fence. The auxiliary fence should be fixed to the rip-fence

Fig. 2.19: The rip-fence and auxiliary fence help to give a constant length for repeat cuts. The auxiliary fence should be set in line with the forward gullets

and its position should be carefully set with two purposes in mind: to provide a cut-off stop so that all the pieces are the same length, and to create a space between the saw-blade and the rip-fence so that the cut pieces can move away from the blade and not jam or kick back. The forward end of the auxiliary fence should line up with the gullets of the teeth at the front of the saw-blade. An extra wooden back-up fence on the crosscut fence will help push the cut pieces well clear of blade and auxiliary rip-fence, as well as minimise break-out or 'spelch' (fig. 2.4). Hold the board firmly against the crosscut fence and the auxiliary fence as you move it towards the blade. As you move the crosscut fence back after the cut is completed, move the wood slightly away from the blade so you don't back-cut the endgrain. This also prevents the blade catching and throwing the wood off the table.

The mitre guide

Larger machines will have a system for altering the angle of the crosscut fence for mitring at angles up to 45°. The smaller ones use a mitre guide, a back plate that swivels on a long metal tongue that slides in the saw-table groove. To check the accuracy of your mitre guide, set the angle at 45° and make a cut; turn one piece over, put the cut ends together and use a try-square to test the right-angle (fig. 2.20). Any error in the setting will be doubled and will therefore show up readily. Adjust the mitre guide setting for error, and you can cut angled pieces with confidence.

Compound mitres are used in cabinet pediments, tapered boxes or any other construction where angled pieces meet without showing endgrain (fig. 2.21). These involve tilting the saw-blade (or, on some machines, the saw-table) as well as setting the mitre guide or crosscut fence (fig. 2.22). On most decent table-saws, the maximum angle of tilt on the saw-blade is 45°. With safety and accuracy as the priorities, several points should be checked before cutting a compound mitre, or indeed any process which involves tilting the saw-blade:

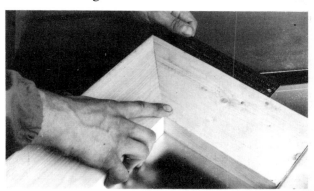

Fig. 2.20: Check the accuracy of your mitre guide by making one cut and seeing if the two pieces make a perfect right-angle

Fig. 2.21: The blade (or table) at one angle and the fence at another give compound mitres like the one *above*. It takes a long time to get it right by trial and error!

Fig. 2.22: Compound mitring with blade and fence both at an angle. The mathematics is by no means simple – use the chart, fig. 2.23

• Will the wood pass under the *lower* edge of the blade top-guard, since the guard tilts with the blade and one edge will be lower than the other?
• As the blade tilts, the saw teeth get closer to the table, so you may have to raise the blade to ensure that the saw teeth are set correctly for the thickness of the wood.

• Remember that with a tilted saw-blade and/or angled fence or table the length of the cut will be far greater than with 90° crosscutting, so allow extra length when preparing the board, and measure very carefully when setting the machine.

Our table of angle (fig. 2.23) for correct setting of the saw-table and mitre guide is for making tapered boxes; but obviously the '4-sided box' column will apply when you want the cut pieces to join at 90° in plan view. If your blade tilts rather than the table, convert by working from the vertical – the standard blade position – rather than the horizontal, which is the standard off which table angles are measured. Thus for a compound mitre at 60° slope, the pieces joining at 90° in plan, the bottom of the column shows the table angle as 21°; for a tilting blade, this means tilt the blade at 21° off the vertical, or 69° from the table.

Cutting tapers

Cutting tapers on, for instance, chair legs in-

Fig. 2.23: Compound mitre chart

Slope	4-sided box		6-sided box		8-sided box	
	Table angle	Mitre guide	Table angle	Mitre guide	Table angle	Mitre guide
5°	44¾°	85°	29¾°	87½°	22¼°	88°
10°	44¼°	80¼°	29½°	84½°	22°	86°
15°	43¾°	75½°	29°	81¾°	21½°	84°
20°	41¾°	71¼°	28¼°	79°	21°	82°
25°	40°	67°	27¼°	76½°	20¼°	80°
30°	37¾°	63½°	26°	74°	19½°	78¼°
35°	35½°	60¼°	24½°	71¾°	18¼°	76¾°
40°	32½°	57¼°	22¾°	69¾°	17°	75°
45°	30°	54¾°	21°	67¾°	15¾°	73¾°
50°	27°	52½°	19°	66¼°	14¼°	72½°
55°	24°	50¾°	16¾°	64¾°	12½°	71¼°
60°	21°	49°	14½°	63½°	11°	70¼°

For example: If you want to make a box with sides inclined 20°, set the blade or table at 41¾° and the mitre guide at 71¼°.
Tilting blades: Measure 'table angle' as saw-blade angle **off the vertical.**

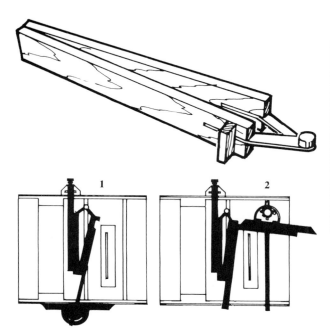

Fig. 2.24: *Top*, the adjustable taper jig, and two ways of setting the angle, *above*. First find the angle you're working to; then set it on the protractor of the mitre guide (*1*) which you then turn over and set against the back of the saw. The table acts as a datum surface. Alternatively (*2*) you can set the mitre guide protractor and use a square off that straight on to the jig

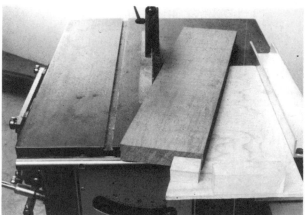

Fig. 2.25: A simple single-step taper jig, ready to roll. Any workpiece must be cut over-length, of course, because cutting from a wide blank like this will mean a feather-edge on the front of the taper

Cutting double-sided tapers with the adjustable jig involves doubling the angle between the hinged sides of the jig after the first taper has been cut.

Cutting wedges

A simple jig is also needed for wedges (fig. 2.26) easily made from a piece of scrap wood with notches cut in the side; wedges must be cut from a wide piece of short-grained wood. The width of the piece is the length of the wedge; cut two or three notches in your jig for wedges of different length. The notches in the jig will present the grain of the workpiece to the blade at an angle, which will give you strong wedges with the grain running down their length. If you cut them with the grain running across, they will snap as soon as you tap them because the fibres will be so short. Adjust the rip-fence so the feather-end of the cut-out in the jig nearly touches the blade, place the wood in the notch of the jig and hold both firmly as you slide the jig along the rip-fence to cut. After each cut, turn the wood over to make the next wedge. Stop before your blank gets too short and brings your fingers perilously close to the edge! A false table of 4 or 6mm ply, clamped over the blade which is then wound up

volves the preparation of a jig, either an adjustable table jig (the hinged type can be bought) or a step jig (figs 2.24, 2.25). If you need to be dead accurate on tapers with the step jig, you can make the width of the step the same as the maximum width of the cut-away section, and run the edge of the step next to the blade. Otherwise, calculate depth of step according to the angle of taper you need, and the width of the whole jig – and thus the position of the rip-fence against which it runs – according to the maximum width of the cut piece and the size of the blank. Remember that for double-sided tapers you will need two steps on your jig.

To cut tapers, hold the workpiece against the upper step of the jig for the first cut and push the wood and jig through the saw together with the jig sliding along the rip-fence. Then turn the workpiece over and cut again with the newly cut taper against the lower step.

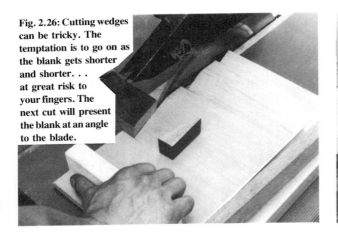

Fig. 2.26: Cutting wedges can be tricky. The temptation is to go on as the blank gets shorter and shorter. . . at great risk to your fingers. The next cut will present the blank at an angle to the blade.

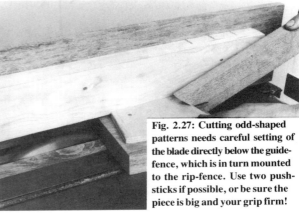

Fig. 2.27: Cutting odd-shaped patterns needs careful setting of the blade directly below the guide-fence, which is in turn mounted to the rip-fence. Use two push-sticks if possible, or be sure the piece is big and your grip firm!

through it while spinning, will stop thin wedges jamming between the blade and the mouth of the table insert.

Cutting an odd-shaped pattern

The success and safety of this operation, like every wood-machining process, depend entirely on preparation. First, make your pattern from a piece of scrap wood so that it is *exactly* the size and shape that you want, and mount it with panel pins on top of the board to be cut. Remove the blade guard and riving-knife (commercial workshops are prevented from doing this by the Woodworking Machines Regulations 1974), and mount a wooden guide-fence on the rip-fence, or on to a high false fence attached to it. Set the guide-fence carefully so that it is just high enough to allow the board being cut to pass underneath, and line the left edge of the guide-fence with the left edge of the kerf of the blade, so the workpiece passes underneath the guide-fence and the blade will cut exactly below the edge of the pattern fixed on top (fig 2.27). It is particularly important with this technique to move small offcuts away from the blade with a push-stick rather than fingers!

You can now cut along the sides of the pattern, using your left hand (if the piece is big enough) or a push-stick to press the wood towards the guide fence, use another push-stick to feed

the work toward the blade. As each edge of the pattern slides along the guide-fence, the work-piece passes underneath the guide-fence and the blade will cut exactly below the edge of the pattern. It is particularly important with this technique to move small offcuts away from the blade with a push-stick.

Rebating and grooving

Cutting rebates (steps along the edge of a board) and grooves are operations which again call for the removal of the blade-guard and riving-knife, which is illegal in a professional shop. Safety and careful preparation must be prime considerations. Short-cuts will result in loss of accuracy, injury to fingers or offcuts jamming and kicking back, so always use *two* push-sticks for these operations.

A rebate is formed by making two cuts, one horizontal and one vertical, along the edge of the board (fig 2.28). Since one of the cuts will be made with the board standing on a narrow edge, mount a high false fence on the rip-fence to act as a support. The high false fence should be made and mounted carefully so that it is perfectly square and vertical; if not, the work will be inaccurate. The best way of keeping legal and safe is to make a 'tunnel-guard' for this job – an upside-down L-shaped box which overhangs the blade and comes hard up to the board, held ver-

Fig. 2.28: Rebating a high board; sprung guards keep the workpiece safely against the fence. Don't trap the small offcut between blade and fence

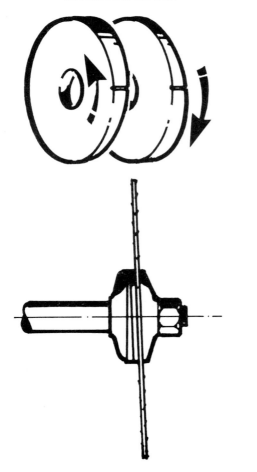

Fig. 2.29: Wobble washers and how they work on a blade arbor

tically as you cut. Otherwise clamp feather-boards – pieces of ply, say 30 x 15in, with long curved cuts from one long edge to about 5in from the other that form springy anti-kickback teeth – to table and fence to keep the board in and down.

When making the second cut to form the rebate, keep the offcut piece on the *outside* of the blade to prevent it jamming against the fence and kicking back. And *don't* stand directly behind the work; if the thin offcut jams between fence and blade it will hurtle backwards at stomach height.

Grooves can be cut in two ways; either in a series of passes over the blade, or in one pass over a blade tilted with wobble-washers (fig 2.29). Two of these large wedge-shaped washers can be fitted to the blade spindle, causing the blade to move left and right as it rotates and thus make a wider-than-usual cut. Remember that the top of the saw-blade moves in a very slight arc, so the bottom of the groove will be slightly curved (fig. 2.30); it also applies if you use wobble washers for tenoning. The finish on the cut is not very flat. There are also dado and grooving saws – blades with cutting edges up to

Fig. 2.30: Remember that the deep face of a 'wobble washer' groove will be slightly curved

¾in thick or sets of blades which you set up at different thicknesses – but these are on the whole not very desirable on a circular saw-table. Far better use the spindle moulder. If you do use them, take great care to fix proper hold-down and guarding systems.

Dropped-in work

Perhaps the most dangerous operation on the circular saw is dropped-in (or set-in) work, where a groove or slot begins or ends (or both) away from the edges of the board. It is for shallow grooves only, and anyway not for the professional, according to safety law. A featherboard, the special anti-kickback fence, should be bolted to the rip-fence, and you should use spring-loaded hold-downs as well. For cuts which start in the middle of the board and run off the end, you will need one back-stop on the end nearest you; for cuts that begin and end inside the edges of the board, two stops are needed, fixed firmly one at each end of the fence. These prevent the work being thrown forward or back.

The safest way of doing this is to experiment with the rise-and-fall of the blade, and work out exactly how many turns will bring the blade up to the height you need.

The featherboard and stops should be positioned carefully. With the workpiece held firmly down on the table by push-stick, featherboard and hand, its back edge against the back-stop, start the saw and wind the blade up to the predetermined height. Push it through to make the cut; if the groove is stopped both ends, the position of the far stop will be dictated by the length of cut. If the cut finishes before the edge of the board, push it to the far stop, turn the machine off while you hold it, wait till you are sure the blade has stopped, then wind the blade down and lift the workpiece away. You should use push-sticks wherever possible for dropped-in work.

Raised and fielded panels

The technique of raising and fielding panels, though best done on a spindle-moulder, can be performed quite adequately on the circular saw. The main limitation is that the saw can only do straight cuts, while the spindle-moulder can produce a wide variety of interesting curved and moulded designs. Again, these operations require the removal of guards, against the commercial-use regulations; you can use tunnel-guards and safety hold-downs or Shaw-type guards, however.

The shoulders of the panel are made first by cutting grooves round the edge of the panel section, using the stop on the crosscut fence to locate the short-side shoulders (fig. 2.31). Then

Fig. 2.31: The blank for the raised and fielded panel (*above*) has had grooves ripped and crosscut to the depth of the shoulder

the saw-blade should be tilted to the required angle to cut the cheeks of the panel. You need a high fence to support the workpiece while it rests on its narrow edges, and a spring system of holding the panel to the fence while you push it. The blades of most table-saw's tilt in only one direction, so the high fence must be bolted to the right-hand side of the rip-fence, looking ahead from behind the blade. Then move the fence to the left of the saw-blade, and feed the panel smoothly through the angled cut (fig 2.32), supported and secured by the tension guards. You

Fig. 2.32: Set the rip fence to the left of the blade (*above*) so the angled teeth will cut just to the grooves. All guards removed for clarity

can buy Shaw guards to fit on most machines, or make your own adaptable featherboards and hold-downs.

Tenoning

There are several ways of making one half of woodworking's favourite joint on the circular saw:

● Make the shoulders first by cutting grooves at the full depth of the tenon; then make the cheeks with a series of passes over the blade (at the same setting), working from the edge inwards towards the groove (fig 2.33). This method is quick and fairly safe but when the workpiece is not completely square the series of

Fig. 2.33: The safest, if most laborious, way of tenoning on the circular saw is to cut the shoulders first and then pass the cheeks back and forth over the blade. Set an auxiliary fence to the centre of the workpiece's height – both sides are cut away

passes leaves a rough finish and possibly a twisted tenon.

• Cut the shoulders first, as before, and then insert a tenoning jig (bought or made) in the table slot (fig 2.34). Clamp the workpiece vertically to the jig so that both will slide smoothly towards the blade to cut the cheeks in one pass. This method is also safe since your fingers need push only the jig – as long as you have proper guarding. There is a disadvantage with this method – tear-out ('spelch') as the blade emerges from the back of the workpiece. This can be prevented by inserting a small backing piece of scrap wood between the clamp and the workpiece on the side nearest you.

• With the workpiece held vertically in a tenoning jig, use wobble washers on the blade spindle to tilt the saw-blade and make a wider-than-usual cut along the edge of the workpiece. This technique has the disadvantage of leaving a slight curve at the top of the cut, which in this case is the shoulders of the tenon, but the tenon is cut in one operation.

• In the absence of a tenoning jig, the tenon cheeks can be cut by clamping the workpiece vertically in a sliding frame which you make and fit over the high false fence. You must design something that covers the blade too.

Panel cutting

Panel products such as hardboard and chipboard usually come in large sheets – and not necessarily with straight edges! Cutting large boards

Fig. 2.34: A proprietary tenoning jig holds the workpiece firmly. A box- or tunnel-guard is essential here; guards removed for clarity

Fig. 2.35: Ripping a sheet of hardboard with a comparatively coarse blade. Laminated chipboard or thin plies will need many more teeth and finer pitch. The size of your sliding table will limit the size of board you can handle comfortably

will mean using all the available table extensions for the machine in order to support the work-pieces. The blade should be set so that one tooth's height shows above the panel (fig. 2.35).

Panel products often suffer from spelch problems. To avoid whiskered edges, get the best saw-blade for the job – fine pitch, neutral or negative hook – and, if possible, use a false table to minimise the gap between blade, table and work. One rather laborious way of overcoming the problem is set the blade to half the thickness of the board, and cut through from both sides. Some machines have little scoring saws in front of the blade, which cut a preliminary line and ensure a clean edge.

CHAPTER 3

The radial-arm saw

With almost all free-standing woodworking machinery, you feed the workpiece towards cutters or blades spinning in a stationary unit. The radial-arm saw is a notable exception to this principle. The radical difference is that the spinning blade is itself pulled over the static workpiece.

A radial-arm saw (fig. 3.1) consists of a worktable (often on four legs), a vertical pillar carrying a horizontal arm that pivots on the pillar, and a saw-blade and motor attached to a sliding unit which moves the length of the arm. The wide range of independent movements of the blade, the sliding unit and the horizontal arm combine to suit a variety of applications; the arm can be raised, lowered and moved around the pillar (fig. 3.2) while the blade and motor can be tilted and rotated (figs 3.3, 3.4). There are also usually facilities to mount a router, router cutters, or moulding and straight cutters on the arm, using either the saw's motor or (in the case of the router) that of the tool itself.

The unique design of the radial-arm saw makes it ideal for crosscutting, particularly when you're handling long pieces that would be awkward on a table-saw. Cuts to a line are quick and easy, because you can just see the edge of the workpiece and the tips of the blade where metal meets wood – and (you hope) your line as

Fig. 3.1: A radial-arm saw with all guards removed. The blade/motor unit rises and falls, slides on the arm and tilts; it's important to get the table set up accurately

well. Most radial-arms are very well guarded (fig. 3.5), with mechanisms that lift the guards over the wood as the blade travels across it (designs vary – some are better than others), but they still allow a convenient visibility factor that

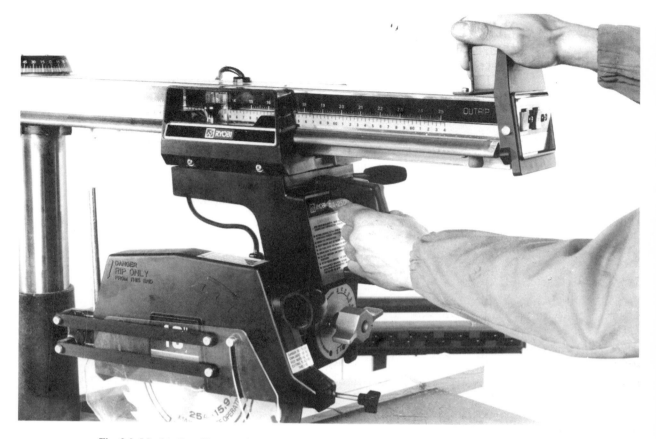

Fig. 3.2: Moving the pillar round sets the saw to cut mitres across the table. Release mechanisms vary

Fig. 3.3: Tilting the motor and blade to cut a mitre in the thickness rather than the width of the work

the table-saw cannot give; crosscutting on a table-saw, the workpiece passing over the blade, demands an awkward craning of the neck, if you're just cutting to a line. The safety aspect is a subject of much controversy, of course, but there remains no doubt that the radial-arm is good news for quick 'one-off' cuts in a busy workshop. It's also efficient for repeat-cutting (fig. 3.6) where a stop-block is clamped to the fence to give an accurate length; again blade-and-line visibility is an advantage. If you're doing a lot of this work, chamfer the bottom edge of your stop-block because dust can collect against it and reduce the length of your supposedly uniform pieces.

There is also an unarguable advantage of the radial-arm saw over the table-saw price. Unless you go for heavy-duty industrial equipment, you will get a versatile and accurate machine for considerably less than a table-saw with comparable capacity and performance.

However, the big argument is over the potential hazards that, some claim, are inherent in the design of the machine. A blade travelling over the top of the workpiece spells all sorts of danger, they say; there is undoubtedly some truth in this, and it pays to be extra careful when you're using a radial-arm. Never let yourself fall into the habit of using it hastily. The blade can 'walk' over the wood, perhaps shifting it, pulling it back and up (and maybe your hand with it), and possibly damaging the machine. Always

Fig. 3.4: Release another mechanism to swing the blade/motor unit on its own axis

Fig. 3.5: Guard designs vary in complexity and efficiency; this transparent plate lifts to clear the wood as it passes the blade

pull the slider smoothly, match the speed of pull to the thickness of the wood, and have the right blade; for crosscutting, a blade with negative rake on the fronts of the teeth, for ripping, the 'positive hook'. If you're cutting bowed material, put the convex side down and/or the rounded edge against the fence so the cut will open up as the blade moves, rather than jam on to it. Have a closer look, if you're considering buying one, at the on/off button – if the blade does jam (and it isn't unusual), you'll need to turn the motor off to get out of trouble. How near your hand (or nose or shoulder) is the switch? If you have to reach round a corner to the switch, it will be difficult to hold the wood while the jammed blade strains to free itself, and turn off. Check to see if there are safety cut-outs, blade brakes, and other desirable features.

The riskiest part of the radial-arm saw, in a sense, is its very convenience. It's just too tempting to slap a piece of wood down and be pulling the blade over it almost before you've shifted your hand . . . no woodworking machine should ever be used carelessly, but safety margins are greater with some than others.

Fig. 3.6: Repeat crosscutting to a pre-set length with a clamped block

Fig. 3.7: A straight mitre cut with the arm swung at 45°. Note the hefty back-fence

Setting up and crosscutting

Careful setting-up of a radial-arm saw is vital to its efficient and accurate performance. This involves sensitive and painstaking installation, to get all the calibrations spot on; almost everything is adjustable, so if a dial says 90° and you're getting an 88° cut, you can sort it out. Start by levelling the table, and then line it with hardboard or a piece of thin ply, making sure no panel pins go in where the blade might travel. Unless you're doing dado or grooving cuts (where the height adjustment is useful), the blade needs to project through the bottom of the wood, and there's no point in replacing the thick ply or chipboard table regularly! The bottom surface of the workpiece must be hard against the table to prevent spelching, so when the hardboard or ply is badly scored, move it around or

replace it. The wooden fence at the back of the table is the same; the blade goes behind it, so blade-width kerfs are cut out of it whenever and wherever you re-position the blade. The notches can be quite useful for positioning pieces to be cut at first, but the inevitable vibration of the blade soon widens them, and you can't rely on this as a system of measurement for long. It's also important to realise that the different angles at which the blade can be set will eventually combine to create a selection of wedges in the fence, ready to be cut loose, jam between the blade and work or fence, bounce off and fly past

Fig. 3.8: A mitre cut with the blade/motor unit at an angle on the wood's thickness

Fig. 3.9: A compound mitre cut

your head – if you're lucky. Wear safety glasses and change the fence when it needs it.

When setting the machine up for use, *read the manufacturer's instructions thoroughly*. Make sure you know exactly how to adjust the machine and its guards, and are familiar with the locking devices and the panic button. Note the direction of rotation of the saw, and make sure it's mounted the right way round. Don't use extra-heavy blades, as they can put a strain on the motor bearings. Do trial runs with the moving parts, getting the feel of how it all works; level up the table, square up the arm to the fence, and check the various cuts for accuracy. The best way of doing this is to cut one piece in two, turn one half over, and see if the two pieces placed end-to-end still make a dead straight line. For mitre cuts (fig. 3.7, 3.8), check that the two halves of one piece cut at 45° go together to make a perfect right-angle. Compound mitres (fig. 3.9), too, are easily done but tricky to set up; the blade itself is working on two angles, given by the arm's rotation and the tilt of the blade/motor unit. Get one dead right and then go on to the other, then check the total effect and work back again, if necessary.

In design terms, it looks as if there are more areas for possible inaccuracy in these machines, because it would be natural for the arm to drop slightly at its extremity, and accuracy be lost at the outer end. While hairline adjustments are more difficult at the saw's limits of extension, the better machines are remarkably dependable, and there is always some correction you can make. There are machines on the market with support for the arm at both ends, but these have other disadvantages.

Ripping

Ripping – cutting along the grain – is a great deal less pleasant on radial-arm saws than cross-cutting, and in truth it is a function to which the design does not lend itself. If you can only afford one saw, however, you can still get reasonably

Fig. 3.10: Panel cutting or ripsawing can be uncomfortable to eyes and face! Blade-guarding and enclosing systems vary in effectiveness

effective ripping; just remember to wear your eye-protectors, because the blade's direction of rotation means the dust and chips fly straight back at you (fig. 3.10). Attempts to extract or deflect airborne waste are only partly successful, because it's difficult to enclose and guard a sliding blade efficiently. Most saws have 'in-rip' and 'out-rip' positions, which basically mean that the motor is either closer to the fence than is the blade for the wider cuts or further away from it for the narrower ones. The blade/motor unit locks anywhere on the arm, and even with the smaller machines you can rip widths up to 24in. Again, be especially safety-conscious; there are grip-teeth devices (fig. 3.11), varying from machine to machine, which prevent kickback of the workpiece, and a safety hold-down should also be incorporated; the natural tendency is for the blade to lift the wood off the table. The height of both these mechanisms (sometimes they are one and the same) is critical for their proper function, which in turn means that the thickness of the wood must be constant. If it varies in thickness, the grip-teeth/hold-down will chatter when it goes loose and jam when it gets too tight. Don't be tempted to save a walk round the table to collect cut pieces by ripping half a length, pulling it back and cutting to make the line meet

Fig. 3.11: The grip-teeth should be just on top of the wood for ripping – not too tight or they will jam. Be sure they are the right way round

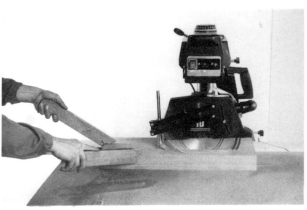

Fig. 3.12: Use two push-sticks if you can

halfway; to do this you'll need to have the safety teeth too loose to do their job properly, and you're asking for your bit of wood to savage you mercilessly. Use two push-sticks (fig. 3.12), remember also that the blade is turning in different directions on 'in-rip' and 'out-rip', and feed the work from the correct end of the table.

Manufacturers claim that the radial-arm saw's undoubted versatility is further enhanced by the capability of carrying grooving and moulding devices, either cutters in blocks or a separately-powered electric router. It's quite a good idea to turn your hand-held router into an overhead machine on the arm of the saw, but the wooden table is not really an accurate enough reference surface for spindle moulding, and the motor and cutter peripheral speeds are too low for the best result. Better than nothing of course, but if you do use these facilities, make a number of small cuts rather than one big one, feed the work quite slowly, and make sure your cutters are in tip-top condition. Also, be sure to get all of your cutting done before you move to moulding or vice versa – these things take time, to change from function to function and get it accurate. In ordinary cutting terms alone, thousands of satisfied radial-arm saw users find they get excellent value from the machine's compactness, convenience, adaptability, and, above all, price.

CHAPTER 4

The planer/thicknesser

As everyone knows, preparation of the raw material is a vital part of the process by which a quality work is produced; you really will never produce good work if the stock you are working with is not perfectly flat and straight on all faces – unless you are a carver or a woodturner, and sometimes even then.

Planing and thicknessing sawn timber produces straight working stock of consistent width and thickness. If you are a comparative newcomer to the idea of machining your own dimensions, you will be used to using timber bought from the yard 'PAR' or planed all round – it should, in other words, be ready to use, but it rarely is. You will be amazed at the design and construction control that planing and thicknessing your own stock gives you; you can specify your own widths and thicknesses, and produce them not only accurately, but also with a high degree of sympathy to the behaviour of the wood under machining, which means that even the stock you start your construction work with will be smoother and flatter than timber bought ready machined.

There are surface planers, which machine straight and flat faces and edges on sawn wood, and there are thicknessers, which plane wood with one or two faces already straightened to a constant thickness. For the purposes of this chapter, we are looking at a combination machine (fig. 4.1), which performs both these functions – though not at once, of course; they vary widely in design, but all work on the same basic principle.

Fig. 4.1: A combined planer/thicknesser, the outfeed table hinged back for thicknessing. Vital dust extraction is also set up

'Surfacing' or 'overhand planing' (for edges this is known as 'edging' or edge-planing', and machines which do only this as 'jointers') requires the wood to be passed along two cast and machined tables – the infeed and the outfeed – over the cutters of a block spinning between them. Adjusting relative table height effects overall straightness and depth of cut. In thicknessing, the wood is passed over a worktable and under a spinning cutter-block, the cutters taking away material from the top to give a constant thickness between the cutting circle and the flat surface of the table. On combination planer/thicknessers, the cutter block is the same; the wood is passed either under or over it.

Cutting theory

To get an idea of how these machines work and to be able to use and maintain them to their highest performance, it pays to have at least a basic understanding of the cutting principles involved. Because the knives (often called 'irons') are spinning in a block – usually two to a block at the level we are discussing, sometimes three or four – their cutting edges meet the wood at an angle, and, passing through a circle, chop out a very slight arc. This is entirely unlike the cutting action of a hand plane, which slices through the wood grain parallel to the surface. Magnified, the surface of a machine-planed piece of timber will look something like fig. 4.2a, and you can actually see this if you hold the piece up in a certain light. Bad machining makes this effect very obvious. Clearly, the knives will be likely to rive deep and split into the grain until the chip breaks as they come up on their circle away from the wood (fig. 4.2b); this is why you can get 'tear-up' on the surface from a thicknesser or planer, and why there are chip-breaking and chip-limiting designs of pressure bars (fig. 4.2c) and cutter blocks (fig. 4.2d); also face-bevel grinding on the cutters themselves (fig. 4.2e) turns the chips and makes them less likely to rive deep into the grain. The pressure bar shown in fig. 4.2c is de-signed specifically for thicknessing; it holds the wood down on the worktable, and also gives downward pressure to help the chips break before the split has gone deep into the grain. It is obvious that different kinds of wood will be more or less likely to tear up, and also that grain direction as you feed it over or under the cutters will make a difference (fig. 4.3). A good finish on your planed surface also depends on sharpness, correctly set knives and tables, correct cutting speeds, and machine sympathy. That is, don't set the cut too deep, don't feed too fast (either hand or powered feed should be regulated according to the job), and remember that a wide cut gives the machine a lot of work to do just as does a deep one.

The machine

The combination planer/thicknesser shown in fig. 4.1 is fairly typical; infeed and outfeed tables on top, the thicknessing table beneath. A vertical long fence, usually adjustable for chamfering angles, sits across the two top tables to give a perfect right angle (or otherwise) to table and cutters; automatic feed and pressure rollers either side of the cutter block inside the machine feed thicknessing work through, resist splintering, and hold the pieces flat to the datum surface of the thicknessing table.

Access to the thicknesser part of such machines varies from model to model; sometimes both tables hinge back, sometimes the outfeed table only hinges up and back, sometimes the surfacing tables both lift off. On the machine in fig. 4.1, the outfeed table hinges away to give you room to feed into the powered feed rollers of the thicknessing end.

It's worth bearing in mind that accurate surfacing is an *absolute prerequisite* of accurate thicknessing, and if tables lift and/or hinge, carefully-adjusted settings can go out. Sawdust and general rubbish can also collect on the surfaces on to which the locating lugs of the tables bear; so make sure all the hinging parts are perfectly

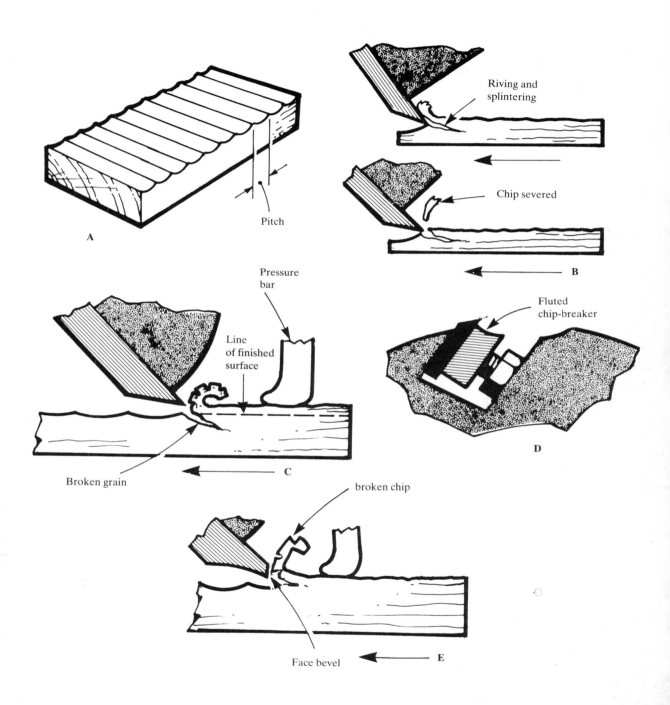

Fig. 4.2: A, a magnified machine-planed surface; B, forward riving and chipping; C, chip turned and cracked by chip limiter and pressure bar; D, a chip-breaker flute in a block; E, a face bevel on a cutter reduces forward rive

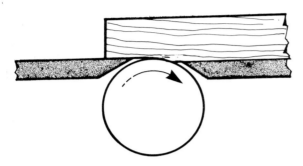

Fig. 4.3: Feeding timber with the grain minimises pickup or breakout

clean whenever you change function from planing to thicknessing and vice versa.

Machine settings are all-important. The infeed and outfeed tables should be perfectly aligned and flat, individually and together, across and lengthways. This must be checked with a straight-edge as soon as you take delivery of the machine. The tables can be adjusted separately, so discrepancies can soon be corrected. If there is a dish or bow in the surface itself, however, send the machine straight back.

Adjustments

Cutters and blocks

Block designs vary quite widely, even amongst the comparatively limited range of machines considered here (fig. 4.4), but for our purposes we only need to look at circular blocks. Vastly

expensive industrial machines use square blocks, but that's another story. The main variations you will find are the methods by which the cutters are held in the block, which also means, of course, the method by which they are adjusted. Look closely at this feature if and when you are buying a machine. Old-type 'slab' or 'cap' blocks (fig. 4.4a) are rare in modern, smallish machines, but you might be buying secondhand, in which case you are quite likely to come across them. They are difficult and frustrating to set up correctly. The vital factor with cutters, of course, is that to do the same work they must describe exactly the same circle, and most modern blocks come with a comparatively easy way of ensuring this. One of the commonest methods is to spring-load the cutters from their back edges, inside the block, and provide an accurately-machined 'jig', a bar on lugs that locate in recesses in the block. You set the knife into the block, finger-tighten the holding screws, set the jig up, then loosen the screws slightly so the spring pushes them out against the jig. Then you tighten the screws up – always from the centre outwards, and always symmetrically. As we have mentioned in the chapters on saws, these processes are easy enough if you are totally methodical, and devise fail-safe routines so you know that the job has been properly done. Let the phone ring while you are changing knives – or take it off the hook. Always

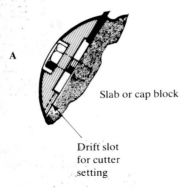

Slab or cap block

Drift slot
for cutter
setting

Wedge bar block (1)

Wedge bar block (2)

Fig. 4.4: Cutter-block designs

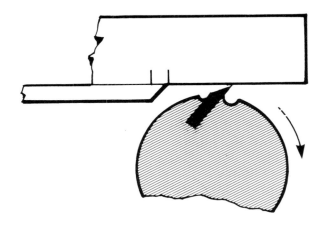

Fig. 4.5: Knives are in the right position when the straightedge moves 2-3mm forward

work with the machine isolated, and go right through the process on all the knives, then check over every one again for tightness. You only need to have a knife fly out of a cutter-block once!

The outfeed table is height-adjustable, of course, so if you have got the knives in exactly the same cutting circle – the tolerances are very fine, hundredths of a millimetre – then you can adjust the outfeed table to line up the cutters' top dead centre (TDC) with the surface. However, unless you have a jig or other foolproof method, it is the outfeed table itself which acts as the datum that tells you where the cutters are coming, so it is against that table that you adjust them.

The time-honoured 'rule of thumb' way of setting up cutters in the block is the 'move the lump of wood' method (fig. 4.5). Make two pencil marks on a perfectly straight piece of wood, 2-3mm apart, then place it on the outfeed table, projecting over the cutters with the first mark on the sharp lip of the outfeed table. Turn the block by hand to check that the highest point of the knives' rotation is at precisely the same level as the outfeed table. The straight-edge should move forward as each knife kisses it so that the second mark comes to rest on the edge of the

table; more and they're too high, less means they're too low. If the blades are set lower than the outfeed table, the wood will hit the near end of the outfeed table because the cut isn't deep enough (fig. 4.6); if they're set higher, the wood will end up with a concave cut over the length, and a 'snipe' at the end where the last few inches leave the lower infeed table, pass over the cutters and drop in before the support of the outfeed table takes effect (fig. 4.7).

As long as you have the cutters doing exactly the same work in the same cutting circle, then you will know if you get either one of these faults that it is the outfeed table height that needs adjusting. There is a situation where the out table can be fractionally high, and although you are getting the work over the cutters on to it, you notice that you are taking far more off at the beginning of the cut than the end. The work is ending up tapered because it rises over the cutters, then balances over on to the high outfeed table, and raises itself too far above the cutters for them to take the same amount consistently.

It should also be mentioned that when you adjust the cutters in the block with the 'move the lump of wood' method, you must check and adjust the cutters right across the width of the table – sometimes a maddeningly frustrating job.

All of which suggests that there must be a

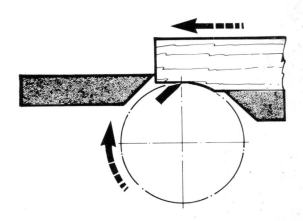

Fig. 4.6: Low knives or a high outfeed table have the same effect – the work will jam and/or end up tapered

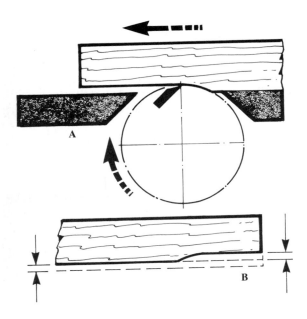

Fig. 4.7: High knives or a low outfeed table will create a concave surface in the work and a 'snipe' at the back (B) where the end drops unsupported on to the cutters

better way, even if you don't have a machine which comes with a knife-setting jig. If the setting is correct, say the pundits of the 'move the lump of wood' method, the straightedge in question will move 2-3mm forward each time a knife kisses it. 2-3mm may be average, but obviously how far the straightedge will move depends on the mass of the straightedge and the block, the speed at which you turn the block by hand, and other mechanical variables.

There is another, easier way, though it will cost you – buy a dial gauge (fig. 4.8). This device, which you can get for about £20 from good tool shops and machinery suppliers, has a spring-loaded contact probe connected to a pointer on a scale, calibrated to read something like from 0-10mm in .01mm graduations. Each complete revolution of the needle represents 1mm, and this is accumulated on a smaller dial. The probe projecting from the bottom of the gauge, when depressed, causes the needle to travel round the dial. On the back is a lug by which it can be attached to a stand.

It is easy to make a simple – but very accurate – right-angle stand from, say, 2x2in hardwood, on which you can mount the gauge vertically for setting up planer knives, and horizontally for checking spindle-moulder cutters, fences and sliding tables. There are various ways of using a dial gauge to the reliable accuracy you need for planer knives, but here is one method:

First, place the stand on the outfeed table with the gauge mounted so the dial is set at a convenient datum, say 2mm. Then check the height of the outfeed table in relation to the cutter-block, and adjust it if necessary to 1mm above the cutter-block; thus the dial should read 1mm when the table is correctly adjusted. Then, with the first knife in position and the holding screws slack enough to allow some movement, adjust the knife until the dial reads the same as the datum 2mm at both ends. This should be done with the knives aligned with the top-dead-centre (TDC) marks on the block housing, but sometimes it's easier to align the contact point of knife and gauge with the TDC mark and then rotate the block minutely to find the highest reading. Once the knives are adjusted and the screws tightened, double-check the setting with each knife aligned at TDC.

All this is done, of course, with the machine isolated from the mains, and in line with recommended safety practice the whole operation is completed in one session without interruption.

Tables and fences

Once the knives are set, the depth of cut is set by lowering the infeed table by the required amount (fig. 4.9). Most machines are calibrated in millimetres (fig. 4.10), and the maximum depth of cut depends on the machine, the thickness of the workpiece and the type of wood. Generally, the finer the grain and the sharper the knives, the slower the rate of feed and the smaller the depth of cut, the finer the finish. You will probably find yourself setting a hefty cut first, where big irregularities in the surface mean

Fig. 4.8: The dial gauge – quick, easy and accurate answer to the knife-setter's problems

Fig. 4.10: Calibration for the thicknessing table is adjustable – but always check the workpiece thickness too. Surfacing-table calibrations should also be checked

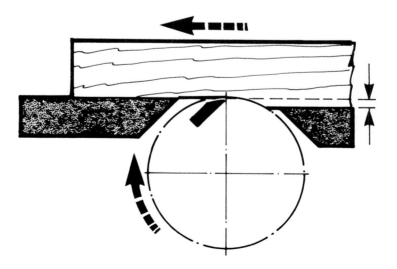

Fig. 4.9: Difference in table-height equals the depth of cut

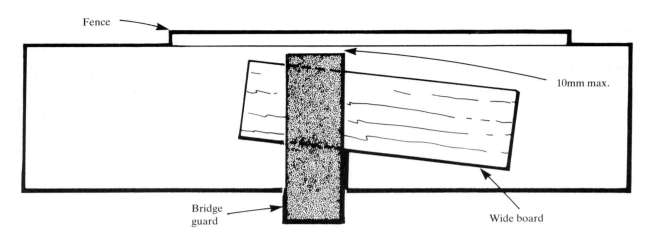

Fence

10mm max.

Bridge guard

Wide board

Fig. 4.11: A wide board is fed at an angle on the surfacer to reduce impact and possible throw-back

only some areas touch the cutters, and as the timber gets flatter, you use finer cuts. Obviously, you can't set too deep a cut with a wide board – you're asking the cutters to do too much work and risking 'throwback' of the board. You can minimise this effect by feeding a board to be surfaced over the top of the cutters at an angle (fig. 4.11), which has the same function as hand-planing with the tool at an angle to the direction of the cut. You can't do this with thicknessing, though; if the rollers don't straighten the work out to go through at 90° to the axis of the cutter-block, then they are out of adjustment and need attention.

For surfacing and edging, if face and edge of the workpiece are to be square to each other, the fence must stand at a perfect right angle to the tables. Use a steel engineer's square to check, remembering that sawdust can get in the way and that fences usually move a little when you tighten the knobs.

Surfacing

You will rarely if ever thickness before you 'surface' or 'face-and-edge' a piece. Before you start work on the planer/thicknesser, carefully examine the piece of wood to be planed. There are three things to look for. First, remove any

foreign bodies in the workpiece; stones, nails, grit – even dust from the floor – can damage and blunt the cutters. Second, look at the grain of the wood. Most grain runs through timber on a diagonal, and the workpiece should be fed into the knives *with the grain sloping in the same direction as the blade movement*, so the cutting action smooths the grain (fig. 4.3). Otherwise the cutters will pick up and tear the grain. Thirdly, look down the length of the piece to identify the concave face and edge. Start with the concave surface down on the tables so the highest parts of the workpiece are removed first, and the ends are cut first (fig. 4.12). If you work the convex side first, there is nothing to stop the wood rocking back and forth as it goes from table to table, and you'll never get a flat face (fig. 4.13). Few pieces of wood, of course, are regularly convex or concave; you have to judge, and often juggle a bit to get the parts you want to cut first.

For maximum safety, as on all woodworking machines, only the minimum amount possible of the cutting blades should be left exposed to prevent accidents to the hands. This means that all the guards should *always* be used. When surface planing (fig. 4.14), the bridge guard should always be in position over the cutter block and at a height which allows just sufficient space for the wood to pass underneath. It's often sensible to

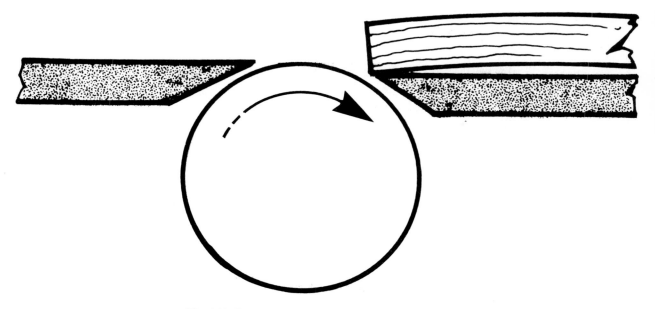

Fig. 4.12: Two bearing points, working with hollow side down

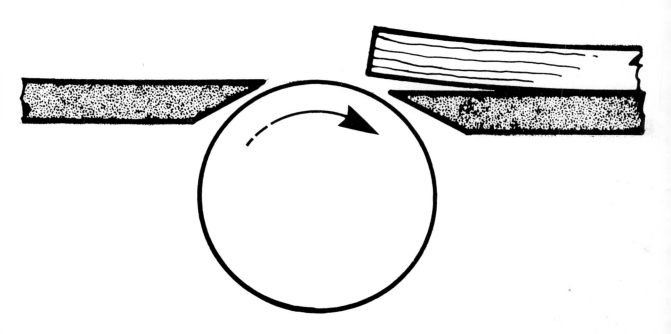

Fig. 4.13: Working round side down causes timber to rock, making it difficult to get a straight parallel face

Fig. 4.14: The guards cover the cutters both sides of the fence

Fig. 4.15: For edging, the bridge guard is moved slightly back, but remains within 10mm of the workpiece

move the vertical fence as close as possible to the near edge of the infeed table so you don't have to lean over the cutters, but they should be guarded anyway. If you do this all the time, of course, you'll wear the cutters unevenly.

For planing edges (fig. 4.15), the workpiece passes between the fence and the guard, so the bridge guard should be set as close as possible to the cutters while allowing a gap no more than 10mm bigger than the width of the wood between fence and guard. Fig. 4.16 shows the minimum gaps suggested by the Woodworking Machines Regulations 1974.

Protection for eyes and ears: it's essential to wear safety glasses or goggles, and ear protectors are strongly recommended, since these machines are noisy, and often kept running for long periods.

Surfacing demands a surprisingly skilful technique. Adopt three positions while feeding a workpiece through: first, both hands should press the wood down firmly on to the infeed table as you push; second, one hand should go over the guard to transfer pressure on to the part of the wood that is now on the outfeed table, while the other hand stays behind, pushing but not pressing down; thirdly, both hands go on the outfeed side, holding the (now flatter) forward end of the work on the outfeed table and pulling through (fig. 4.17). Edging requires a somewhat different technique: the forward hand particularly must press in towards the fence as well as down on the outfeed table (fig. 4.18). You need sensitive fingers because you must register the machined and therefore flatter parts of the work on the datum surfaces of outfeed table and outfeed side of the fence. The aim is always to get the pressure on to the outfeed table as soon as possible, because the outfeed side of the piece on each pass is the 'truer' side. If you press down on the infeed table, the forward end (if it gets over the cutters) will lift away from the outfeed table, and you'll end up with a tapered workpiece. You almost always have to make several passes of the same surface or edge over the cut-

1 **Surfacing**

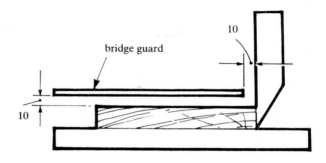

2 **Edging**

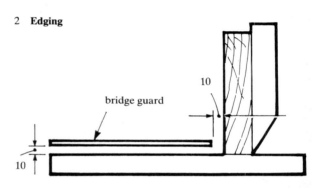

3 **Face-and-edging**

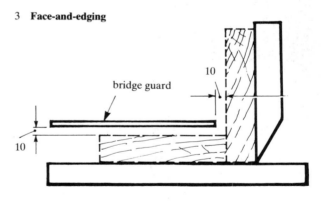

Fig. 4.16: The minimum gaps suggested by the Woodworking Machines Regulations 1974

Fig. 4.17: Surfacing: top, press hard on the infeed table; middle, transfer pressure; bottom, the outfeed table gives the trued surface

Fig. 4.18: Edging: top, the fence is the datum surface – keep the trued face hard against it. Middle, pushing in and along; bottom, forward hand presses the work against fence and outfeed table

ters, according to the roughness, or curve and twist of the wood. When you eye your piece before you start, estimate how much you'll lose before you get it flat and straight full length; if your cutting list allows it, you can cross-cut long pieces to minimise curvature and therefore waste.

Having said all this, think about it again if you're planing thin wood which bends under your hand pressure. Don't press it down at all on the infeed table; it will bend and be cut, then spring back to its original shape. You must let it cut under its own weight, not pressing down on the infeed side, and only gently on the outfeed.

To cut bevels and chamfers on the planer, the fence can be set at any required angle between 45° and 90° (fig. 4.19). Remember that with the workpiece being planed at an angle, you will have to set the infeed table rather lower than for simple surfacing work. Again, set the guard carefully to allow just enough room for the workpiece to pass between the guard and the tilted fence. Also, as suggested in Chapter 1, this operation is much safer if you have an extra fence to stop the work sliding down the angled fence.

Rebates can also be cut on the planer, width and depth depending on size and power of machine. Set the fence to give the required width of the rebate, adjust the infeed table to the correct depth and feed the wood through, pressing continuously against the fence. Make more than one pass at different setting if you have to take big bites, and remember machine safety.

Fig. 4.19: Chamfering. Careful with the guards, and remember you'll need extra depth of cut

As you will often be planing and then thicknessing a number of pieces of wood, it is good practice to stack the wood methodically according to a system so you know which pieces have been done and which haven't at a particular setting. Mark endgrain, so you can see what's what in the stack, and the marks don't disappear once they've been through the machine. If you're preparing a series of workpieces of different sizes, it's best to do the biggest first and keep re-setting the machine in sequence from larger to smaller dimensions. Planning work like this is particularly useful in relation to thicknessing; re-setting will simply mean winding the table up underneath the cutter block. Having a system will save a lot of machine-setting time, and you will also be able to identify very quickly all the pieces to

be thicknessed to the same depth. Also, once you've got true faces and edges and are ready to go to thicknessing, mark all your true surfaces! Be sure to check everything carefully before you change settings or functions; having to go back on yourself wastes time, and it's often impossible to get a setting exactly the same as it was.

Working with short pieces of wood on this machine presents a number of dangers: apart from the threat to fingers getting very close to the cutters, the cutters will tend to draw short pieces into the works and chuck them out again at high speed. To plane short pieces, *always* use a jig or pushblock which covers the workpiece and applies forward as well as downward pressure (fig. 4.20). On the thicknesser, never use workpieces shorter than the distance between the infeed and

Fig. 4.20: A holding block must always be used for short pieces

Fig. 4.21: Only good good thick pieces should be thicknessed to width

outfeed rollers. You must establish this when you get your machine, and always add a few safety inches to the minimum workpiece length.

Thicknessing

Like the planer, the thicknesser needs to be set carefully to get accurate results. In front of the cutter block, the serrated feed rollers grab the wood and feed it steadily under the cutter-block; as with surfacing, you mustn't make too deep a cut in one pass, but there are also drawbacks to making too shallow a cut. Feed rollers can leave their impression on the surface of the wood, which won't be cut away if the cut is too shallow – experiment to establish your minimum – plus sometimes the cut will be so shallow that even

the feed rollers don't grab, and the wood stays in the machine. You have to lower the table to extricate it.

Thicknessing timber obviously needs an established datum surface. The true face you have planed is invariably run on the feed table, and the cutters cut the unplaned side to the set thickness, perfectly parallel to that planed face. You can use a thicknesser to give you width – passing the pieces through on edge – but you must be sure the timber is sturdy enough not to bend under the pressure of the rollers (fig. 4.21). If you do thickness to width, do it first because you will then be moving the table up at every re-adjustment.

There is a limit to how close the table can go towards the cutters, and for thicknessing very

Fig. 4.22: A holding-jig for thicknessing polygonal shapes. It must be firmly held on to the table

Fig. 4.23: Note the extraction hood – a matter of safety, not cleanliness. Thicknessing goes quicker with two people

thin pieces of wood (say, 4mm or less) you must make a false bed out of strong plywood, preferably covered with a plastic laminate like Formica. These materials have a guaranteed consistent thickness and will therefore maintain the accuracy of the machine while stopping the workpiece bending, cracking and exploding under the pressure of the rollers and cutters.

Polygonal workpieces can be planed and thicknessed, with accurate (and safe!) jigs and V-groove beds. Jigs must fit exactly over the thicknessing table so they don't move as well (fig. 4.22).

Machine sympathy is very important on the planer/thicknesser. Hard woods and wide work-

pieces give the cutters a lot of work, so don't try to take off too much wood in one pass. Experience will also show you your minimum depth of cut. Don't push a whole clutch of pieces through the thicknesser at one go; they can jam or ride up over each other. Sectional feed rollers make this more viable, but it's still not good practice. If the differences in size are too great, you'll also get some uncut ones while others are being damaged because the cut is too much.

Feed speed is important, and also needs a sympathetic approach; the slower you push it through, the finer the finish. Thicknessing feed rollers may have adjustable speeds; machines have two, three or four-knife blocks, and obviously the more knives, the finer the finish. More time-consuming to set up, though. Always keep the knives in pairs (or threes) so they're re-ground at the same time and stay in balance. The cutter-block takes a lot of weight at a high speed – it needs balance!

Extraction is a necessity with planer/thicknessers (fig. 4.23). There is usually a hood that comes with the machine, but you must make one if not (see Chapter 9 on Dust extract-

ion). The works will jam up very quickly if the large volumes of waste these machines produce aren't removed – and chips can find their way on to pieces being thicknessed and damage the surface, pressed in by the rollers. Besides, the regulations actually require planer/thicknessers to have extraction, and what the regulations are really about is good practice – which means safety.

CHAPTER 5

THE BANDSAW

While sawing in a straight line is basic to all wood-machining, there comes a point when the woodworker wants a free hand. The bandsaw is the machine that allows you to wander from the straight and narrow in order to cut curves, circles and odd-shaped patterns, as well as the familiar straight line. We have put it after the planer/thicknesser because, except in comparatively unusual circumstances, you work with planed stock on a bandsaw; in many cases, sawing on the table or radial-arm machines is in preparation for the planer/thicknesser.

Bandsaws come in all sizes. Larger models are floor-standing, smaller ones can be bench-mounted, and a 'small' two-wheeled type like the one in the photograph (fig. 5.1) is best mounted on a low table. Huge individual band 're-saws' are for converting log-sized timbers. Whatever the size, they all operate on the same principle: a narrow steel band with one toothed edge runs continuously around two (or three) large rubber-lined wheels (fig. 5.2). The saw, held under tension, cuts as the lower, driving wheel (usually mounted directly on the motor) pulls it down through the workpiece.

The top wheel is adjustable, and getting its tracking and tension right is essential. Before you start work, read the manufacturer's instructions carefully and make sure you know how to make all the adjustments.

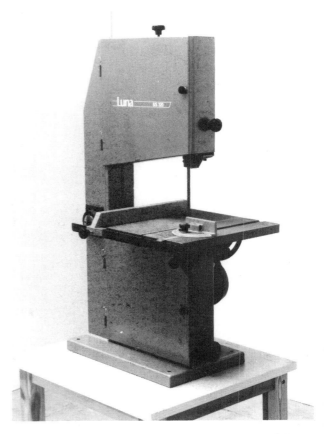

Fig. 5.1: A two-wheel machine offers you greater capacity and easier blade adjustment, at the expense of price and space.

Fig.5.2: Doors open to reveal the works

Fig. 5.3: Adjusting the blade tension with the knob on top. Hold the blade mid-way between table and top-guard; it should move about ¼in either way

Setting up

The tension of the blade is dependent on the position of the top wheel, usually adjusted by a knob on top of the machine (fig. 5.3). The tension should allow about 6mm (¼in) sideways movement of the blade (either side of centre) when you hold it in the middle of the outside run between the wheels and move it from side to side. This is so for all sizes of blade, apart from the massive industrial ones which need 9mm movement. Have the upper guard assembly raised to maximum height to check the tension. Correct blade tension is very important: if it's too loose, the blade will wander, or worse, come off the wheels; if it's too tight, it will snap, usually at the point where the two ends of the band are brazed together. Raise or lower the top wheel to achieve the right tension, and remember that saws that have been broken and repaired will be shorter, so the top wheel will need to come down a bit.

The tracking of the blade needs a careful eye to check that the blade always runs over the central part of the wheel, known as the crown. Turn the wheel by hand to ensure that the tracking is consistently central throughout the wheel move-

Fig. 5.4: All switches off? Then spin the wheel by hand to see how the blade tracks. A knob at the back adjusts

Fig. 5.5: Blade-guides should be fractionally off the blade.

ment (fig. 5.4), don't adjust it with the machine running under power. A knob in the back of the top-wheel housing tips the wheel back or forth. Also be sure that the thrust-wheels and blade-guides aren't bearing on the blade when you check the tracking.

Once blade tension and tracking are checked and adjusted, you must set the blade-guides and thrust-wheels, or bearings, above and below the table (figs 5.5, 5.6, 5.7). This setting should be checked each time you use the bandsaw and whenever you make any other changes or adjustments to the wheels and blades; there are various designs of guides and bearings, which

usually need an Allen key or a spanner to set them. Roller-bearing types are best; on cheaper machines you might have wooden guides and a fixed thrust pad, the face of which will very rapidly be grooved by the back of the blade. Remove the guards, and set the thrust-bearings 1mm behind the blade. The blade should touch them when it's cutting, with enough pressure to make them turn: if the blade is set too tight against them, they will score, and the blade will overheat; if it doesn't touch the thrust-wheels, the blade will be bending too much. Set the guides fractionally off the body of the blade, just behind the gullets of the teeth. They prevent wander; make sure there's no rubbing from one side or the other.

Keep the upper thrust-and-guide assembly as close to the workpiece as you can when you cut. It helps accuracy, and is a precaution against accidents, because the guards usually move up and down with the assembly to keep the blade covered. Another safety feature you will find on more expensive machines is a blade footbrake.

These setting procedures should be followed carefully. Adjusting two-wheel models is easier than it is on three-wheel machines, which can be tricky because two of the three wheels adjust, and affect each other. Generally, three-wheel saws give greater throat depth for smaller overall height, and they can accommodate wider pieces of wood than a two-wheel type of equal height. They are cheaper and usually less robust; more convenient for finer work, but if you can afford it, two wheels are better.

Blades

Selecting the right saw-blade is also important. In general terms, bigger pieces of wood need wider blades with fewer teeth per inch (tpi). The most commonly used blades are in ¼, ½ and ¾in sizes (often metric), though anything from 3mm to 20mm is available. Narrower blades with more tpi are best for small, thin workpieces and for cutting tight-radius curves, while the wider blades are better for straight and deep cuts. Blades with hardened teeth are

Blade width in mm	Minimum cutting radius
6	20
10	45
12.5	55
16	75
20	100
25	180
32	260
40	380

Figs. 5.6 and 5.7: Set the thrust-wheels about 1mm behind the blade

Fig. 5.8: Deep cutting with a high auxiliary fence

common now, which last well but are more expensive and more brittle. They can be sharpened, but that too costs more. It's a matter of taste which you use, but sharpening and setting bandsaw blades is a job for a skilled saw doctor.

Bandsaw wheels move quite slowly, but the critical factor is cutting speed, or the speed of the teeth past a given point – the 'surface speed'. 2000m/min is optimum, but this will vary with motor speed and blade size.

To get the best result, you should have at least three teeth in the workpiece – to cut a ½in board for instance, use a blade with six to eight tpi. In any case, the thickness of the workpiece should always be more than the pitch of (the distance between) the teeth. The main problem with fine blades is that the sawdust doesn't clear and the blade can clog up. Choosing too fine a blade can also cause it to wander, especially when you are ripping along the grain. Other causes of poor cuts from wandering blades are insufficient blade tension, feeding the work too quickly, incorrect setting of blade-guides and badly set or sharpened teeth. Most of these faults cause the blade to heat up, which of course makes matters worse.

Cuts, fences and jigs

A major advantage of the bandsaw is that it can make much deeper cuts than a tablesaw, which with a 12in blade would only have a maximum depth of cut of about 4in (102mm). A medium-size floor-standing two-wheel bandsaw will cut to a depth of 10 or 11in (255-275mm). Bandsaws are good for cutting veneers off large stock, or slicing pieces of which you need to make maximum use of the thickness, since the narrow kerf of the blade allows you to cut very economically (fig. 5.8).

The bandsaw is popular with carvers and woodturners, who use it for preliminary roughing out, or cutting a blank ready for the lathe. Tilting work-tables plus a mitre guide also provide a speedy method of making compound mitres (fig. 5.9) although some loss of accuracy inevitably results from not having such a solid blade.

'Spelch' (breakout) is rarely a problem with the bandsaw since the teeth are comparatively fine and the blades thin. When it does happen, check the wooden insert in the table. If it's worn, renewing it will help. Other causes could be too coarse a blade or too high a rate of feed. When you are cutting curves, work out the line carefully in relation to grain direction, because cutting across too much short grain will make a rough finish and possibly a weak component.

The bandsaw can be used for plastics, metal, and other materials with the right blade; it is a comparatively safe machine, but don't be lulled into forming careless habits. Always use push-

Fig. 5.9: Compound mitres are possible, but not so accurate as with a table-saw

sticks when practicable, especially during ripping (fig. 5.10). Safe crosscutting is shown in fig. 5.11, with the mitre guide backing up the workpiece.

For ripping tall pieces or cutting veneers off blocks, a high false fence – accurately squared – should be attached to the rip-fence of the band-saw table (fig. 5.8). With deep cuts like these, the wood *must* be fed relatively slowly towards the blade because the large amount of sawdust in the cut needs time to clear. Develop a sense of blade sympathy; if you feed the work too fast, overheating will result.

An important part of knowing how to use high fences for deep cutting is understanding the phenomenon of blade 'lead'. For whatever reason, however well the blade is sharpened and set, it is almost inevitable that the blade will lead a cut at an angle to its wide dimension – either towards or away from the fence. You must make a few trial cuts on pieces of scrap to see which way the blade you have set up is leading, and then adjust the fence at a greater or less angle across the table so that it sits parallel to the direction of the cut. This is why high false fences are best made as independent devices, well constructed from solid stable material with convenient clamping areas, so you can clamp them to the table and not have to rely on the proprietary fence for location. Don't try and force the blade to cut where you want it to go – if it wants to lead, let it – and follow.

The bandsaw's controllability and comparative 'finger-friendliness' makes it a good machine for making cuts at angles to the grain – wedges and tapers, for example. Wedges are easily made using a notched jig and a wide piece of short-grained wood (fig. 5.12). Place the wood in the notch of the jig and slide the two towards the blade, the jig against the rip-fence. The blade will cut off a small long-grained wedge, the grain running from the narrow to the wide end. Turn the main piece over after each cut to get a series of identical wedges.

When you cut irregular stock like firewood,

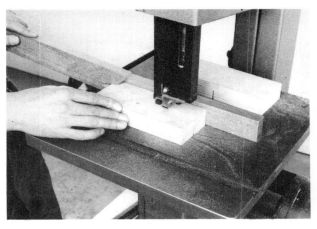

Fig. 5.10: Ripping along the grain with rip-fence and push-stick

Fig. 5.11: Crosscutting with mitre fence behind the work and blade-guide assembly down close to it

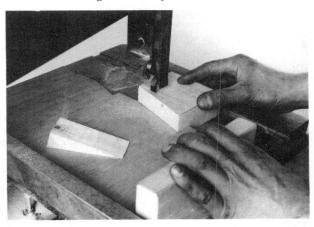

Fig. 5.12: Make a jig with two or three steps in it for wedges of different lengths

there's always a risk that the workpiece will trap in the blade as there is no flat side to press on to the table. For safety's sake as well as for accuracy, it is essential to place the stock in a V-groove jig with wedges to support it (fig. 5.13). You'll have to go through the front edge of the jig, obviously, so make it strong enough to hold together from the back.

Remember – when using jigs near the blade, make sure that nails and screws are well clear of its path.

Tenoning

When cutting tenons, accuracy is of prime importance. These points will help.

- Use a wide blade for vertical consistency and accuracy
- Cut the shoulders first, using a block clamped to the table as a length-stop (fig. 5.14)
- Re-set the saw to cut the cheeks (fig. 5.15), remembering which side of the blade you are measuring to and which side you are cutting to. Clamp the block on to the table to act as a stop, but not where it will get in the way of the offcuts. Set an auxiliary fence in line with a point just past the back of the blade to ensure that the offcuts from the tenon-cheeks can be moved safely away.

It's a good idea to cut a haunch on the top or bottom of the tenon, again using the auxiliary fence and the clamped block as a length-stop

Fig. 5.13: Use a strong V-jig for cutting firewood and other irregular-shaped pieces

Figs. 5.14, 5.15, 5.16, *Clockwise from top left*: cutting tenons needs a wide blade for vertical accuracy. Set a stop and cut the shoulders; reset it, and use an auxiliary fence for the cheeks so the waste won't jam; re-set for the haunches

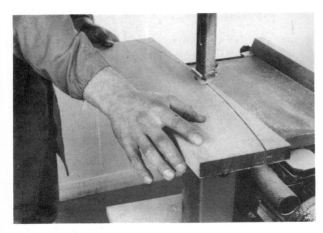

Fig. 5.17: Cutting curves freehand is best controlled with the workpiece firmly held at both ends

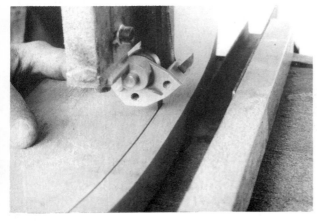

Fig. 5.18: Once you have a curve, reproducing it (fairly roughly) is no problem with the auxiliary fence

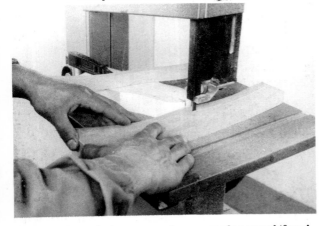

Fig. 5.19: Reproducing compound curves needs a curved 'fence' of tighter radius than any of the ones on your workpiece

(fig. 5.16). This gives more strength to joints at the corners of any kind of frame that takes some strain.

Curved work

You can make light work of copying curves as well as cutting them. Cut the first curve freehand (fig. 5.17). If it's relatively shallow, it can be copied very easily by using the auxiliary fence. Set it so it is only a tooth's depth past the front of the blade, leaving a gap of the required width. Feed the curved edge of the workpiece through the gap between the auxiliary fence and the blade, pressing the curved edge continuously against the fence, which should be the only point of contact (fig. 5.18).

Copying curved shapes where an internal curve comes between two external ones can present problems. The straight fence used in the method of copying simple curves won't allow for internal curvature, so the first step is to cut a curved 'fence' with a tighter radius than the one you are trying to copy (fig. 5.19). The tighter curvature of the 'fence' provides space to manoeuvre the workpiece round the fence as you feed it into and away from the blade. Mark an arrow on the tight-radius fence to show the point nearest to the blade, and set this arrow just 2mm (or the depth of the teeth) from the near edge of the blade. Feed the curved edge of the workpiece towards the blade, pressing continuously against the arrow marked on the 'fence'. This must be the only point of contact throughout the cutting procedure in order to achieve maximum accuracy. Even so, this method is really only good enough for rough copies.

Cutting circles and rings can also be done neatly on the bandsaw, with a little thoughtful preparation. Clamp a baseboard to the worktable; if possible, use an exact square as the workpiece and find its central point by drawing its diagonals. Then pin or secure the central point of the square to the baseboard so that it rotates on top and overhangs slightly on one

Fig. 5.20: A square blank set up on a baseboard and centre-pinned ready for circle cutting

side. Set the workpiece and baseboard on the table so that the shortest distance from the centre of the workpiece (the middle of a side, not a corner) overhangs the edge of the baseboard and touches the bandsaw blade (fig. 5.20). Feed the wood carefully towards the blade by rotating it around the central point (fig. 5.21). Careful feeding is vital here; if you try to go too fast the blade will twist, and apart from not cutting an accurate circle, it's likely to snap.

If the workpiece is not square, pin through a point as near to the centre as you can get to the baseboard. Then set it on the table so the blade will first cut the side which is the shortest distance from the centre. You must use the side nearest to the centre, or the blade will fail to cut

a perfect circle because the other sides of the workpiece won't reach it.

Wooden rings are cut from circles. Mark an inner circle on a circular blank to give the ring width, then cut through the ring area along the grain, and cut round the inner circle (fig. 5.22). The central waste area will then drop out. A cut-through point running along the grain will glue back together strongly, but insert a strip of veneer or wood the same width as the kerf in order to keep the ring's shape as accurate as possible.

Tight curves and internal corners can be tackled in several ways on the bandsaw; see the table at the beginning of this chapter for the tightest radius a given width of blade will cope with. The most common method of cutting a

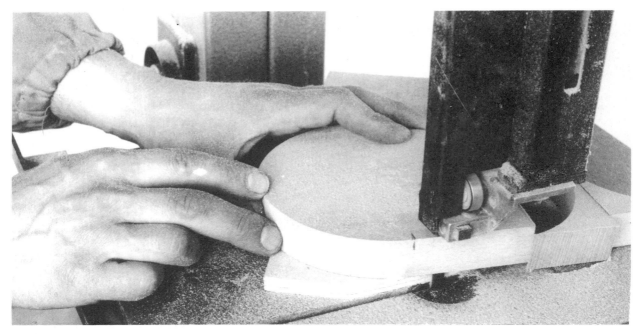

Fig. 5.21: Using a circle-cutting jig, centre the blank so the blade just cuts the flat sides, and line the centre up with the front of the blade

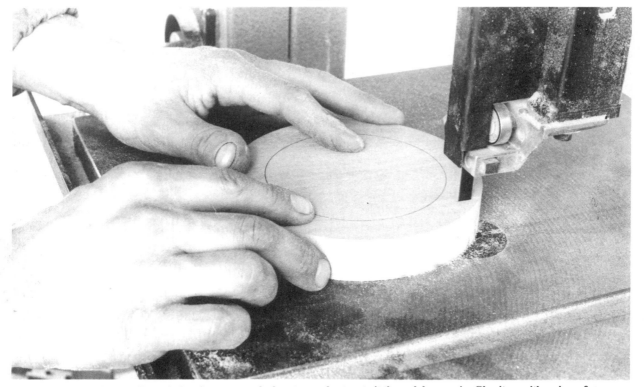

Fig. 5.22: For rings, scribe a circle using your marked centre, and cut on to it through long grain. Glue it up with a piece of veneer

Fig. 5.23: Getting round a tight corner to cut out a straight notch. Be gentle when you take these little bites, and *don't* pull the blade back in the cut

tight curve is to take little bites back and forth to ensure that the blade has enough room to go round the final tight curve. A warning – don't pull back too far in a cut, or try to pull the blade right out of a cut; you'll pull the blade off the wheels. For perfect internal corners, first cut along the straight lines going into the workpiece. Then make a curve round the first corner (again making several small cuts if necessary) and cut along the back internal line into the second corner. Remove the tiny waste piece left from the curve in the first corner with a final straight cut along the back line to meet the cut already made (fig. 5.23).

The bandsaw is also useful for cutting curves in two planes, for example, when making cabriole legs or cutting carving blanks. Again careful preparation will make the process simple and safe. The first step is to mark out two profiles of curves or shapes on squared paper. Transfer the curves to two adjoining sides of the workpiece, and cut out the curve on one side; then pin or tape back the waste in its original position, making sure that there are no pins likely to foul the blade on the second cut. Cut the other profile. Fixing back the waste like this makes it easier to get an accurate second cut, as you are still working with a flat-edged workpiece. Another way of achieving this is to mark and cut the curves on the blank with the blank overlength, making sure that you don't end-cut the waste right off. The first cut pieces will stay on the blank until you have made the second cuts, then you can cut the blank to length and all the waste will fall off in one go.

These are but a few of the techniques and processes you can undertake on the bandsaw. It is a remarkably versatile machine, and comparatively safe to use; only your imagination will limit the jigs and tricks you can devise. But don't ask it to do jobs it isn't designed for, and don't allow its low cutting speeds to make you complacent and forget safety rules.

CHAPTER 6

THE SPINDLE MOULDER

Of all individual woodworking machines, the spindle moulder offers perhaps the greatest potential to the creative woodworker (fig. 6.1). It's held in great affection because it works with a special combination of power and ease; it doesn't just cut. It will make grooves, rebates, and any imaginable moulded profile; it is just about indispensable for producing and decorating curved components in quantity (fig. 6.2). It's the machine whose full use demands not just sympathy and skill, but also a touch of art. The range of work it can handle includes straight and curved moulding, tenoning, notching, corner jointing, scribing mortise-and-tenons, reeding

and fluting, and panel raising; rebating and grooving are just the bread-and-butter.

The basic design of the spindle moulder is very simple. A vertical spindle (the commonest size is 30mm) protrudes through a horizontal worktable, below which is a drive motor which rotates the spindle at high speed (usually in a range of 4-10,000rpm). The shaft can be raised or lowered, and extra choice of working (cutting) height from the table is given by different-sized spacer washers which fit over the shaft. A vast range of cutters and cutter-blocks, heavy precision-machined pieces of steel in which they locate, can be mounted on the spindle – straight, curved, or shaped (fig. 6.3) – and as the spindle rotates and the workpiece is pushed past it along fences, the mould or cut is produced.

Cutters flew out of blocks far more often in the past than nowadays. The spindle moulder has a label as the most dangerous machine in the workshop, largely because of careless setting up; the real danger area of the machine is that work is often hand-fed, and for a deep cut the knives have to protrude a comparatively long way out of the fences. The safety devices that you need for each task must always be set up; never start a job without them. All woodworking machines are potentially dangerous and must be used correctly, but the spindle moulder demands meticulous attention during setting up. The methodical approach to checking and re-

Fig. 6.1: The spindle moulder, with sliding table and adjustable fence plus extraction

A close-up of fences, guards and a home-made featherboard

checking the procedures is doubly important for safety, because there are a number of nuts and bolts you must make sure are tight.

Blocks

The most common accident with spindle moulders by reputation, and probably by fact, can be almost completely eliminated these days – a cutter flying out of a block. Fear with the machine can be as counter-productive as over-confidence, but it pays to have a healthy respect

for it, born from the knowledge that flying cutters have cut people well nigh in half. 'Safety blocks' come in many designs (fig. 6.4a, 6.5), all based on the principle that a wedging system, along with set-screws and locating lugs in the cutters themselves, will hold the cutters in all circumstances. The chip limiters shown in fig. 6.4a also make a difference, preventing the cutters from digging into the work. It's not uncommon for a medium to expensive machine to come with a safety block as standard equipment, although you will almost certainly need other

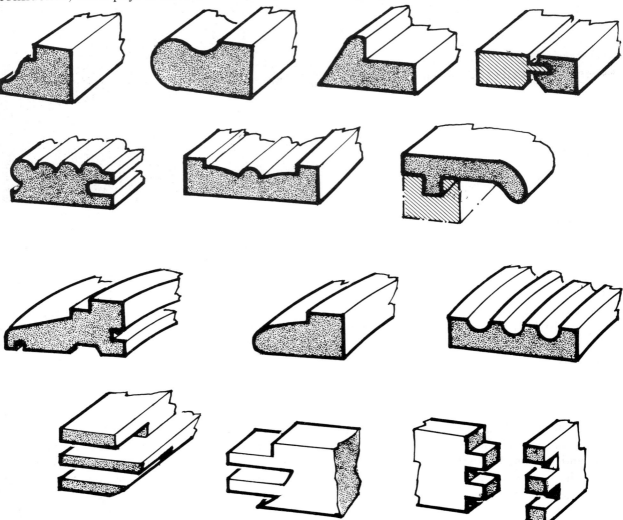

Fig. 6.2: A small selection of the myriad effects you can create with a spindle moulder

Fig. 6.3: A bewildering but beautiful array of bits and pieces includes the angled fence and sliding table (above left), a bonnet-guard and ring fence (right) and an enormous one-piece slotting cutter on the shaft. In front are other cutter designs

ones as your spindle-moulding career progresses.

It's equally unlikely that you will have much need of a 'French head' (fig. 6.4b), which used to be extremely common in industry. It is not really a block at all, but a slotted shaft which holds a single piece of steel, ground to shape at both ends. Obviously, the shape and location of the cutter have to be perfectly balanced for safety and efficiency; centred perfectly, and the shapes ground at each end perfectly reproduced. The steel should never protrude from the shaft more than 50mm either side. French heads were and are used mostly for shaped work in which the normal fences cannot be set up, and quite often the work being moulded would run against the spinning shaft itself. Generally a hairy operation, and thankfully now far less common.

One of the block designs that you will almost certainly come across is the 'Whitehill', which takes cutters in machined slots cut tangentially to the block; they are held in by adjustable flat-faced fillets, which tighten up against the cutter with set-screws. It is flat-to-flat that holds the cutter in here; cleanliness of both cutter and bearing surfaces in the block is vital. Always clean muck off these surfaces with methylated spirit before you mount the cutters. Again, perfect balance and exactly equal projection is important, but if you are making small cuts with light cutters, it is occasionally acceptable to balance one cutter with a blank of equal weight in the other slot. It keeps the spinning block in balance but does no actual cutting. Since only one cutter is doing the work per revolution, low feed speeds are a must.

Rebate blocks (fig. 6.4d, 6.6) are one-

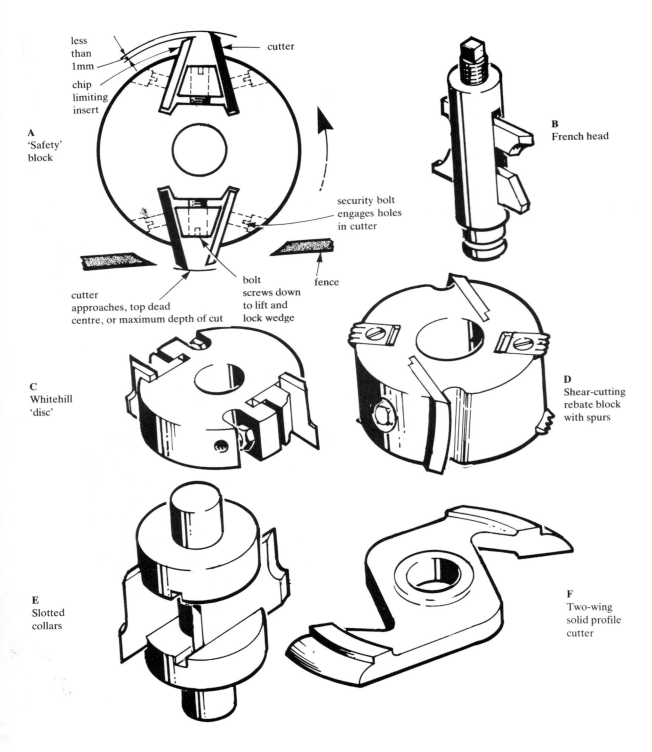

A 'Safety' block

less than 1mm

chip limiting insert

cutter

security bolt engages holes in cutter

fence

cutter approaches, top dead centre, or maximum depth of cut

bolt screws down to lift and lock wedge

B French head

C Whitehill 'disc'

D Shear-cutting rebate block with spurs

E Slotted collars

F Two-wing solid profile cutter

Fig. 6.4: Some of the basic block designs, including the French head

function pieces which carry square-shaped cutters, either tungsten carbide or high-speed steel, some of them have little wing cutters top and bottom for a clean finish above and/or below the cut. The cutters themselves, which are often disposable, project only slightly out of the block, and the design allows the block itself to go deep into the work. They often come with a set of bearing guides of varying diameters which fit on the shaft over or under the block – very useful for curved work, and sometimes even straight. They can be as much as 100mm deep.

Slotted collars (fig. 6.4e) are more common in industry than the small professional or semi-professional workshops (and serious amateurs!) which use comparatively small spindle moulders. They are for very deep cutters which would not fit safely on a normal 'safety' or Whitehill block, and again, perfect balance, of location and shape of the cutters is paramount. Fig. 6.4f shows an example of a two-wing solid profile, or integral, cutter, which is neither a cutter nor a block, but both. A very large one can be seen mounted on the shaft of the machine in fig. 6.3. This and an enormous range of designs on the same principle combine weight and balance of the block with the cutting profile itself, in the form of brazed high-speed steel or tungsten carbide tips. They are again for very specific uses, but there are some multi-profile designs with which you can vary the effect by altering the height of the shaft or depth of cut. One like this can be seen at work on the machine in fig. 6.7.

As far as blocks go, this is just the beginning.

Fig. 6.5: One design of safety-block; lugs on the screw-tightened wedges hold the cutters

Fig. 6.6: A rebate block with double-edged throwaway tungsten cutters, and wing cutters top and bottom

You can pay £300 for a single raised-and-fielded panel integral block, 12in diameter, with a selection of changeable TCT cutters; you can buy slotting and grooving saws, whose two cutting halves are separated by shims of different thicknesses for different widths of groove; you can buy special edge-jointing cutters which impart a matched keying profile to meeting edges of your narrow boards for built-up construction. As your work grows, your shopping list grows – but there is also the fascinating and challenging machinist's art of designing your own mouldings and grinding cutters for your own specific purposes.

Cutter profiles

Apart from the proliferation of cutters of

Fig. 6.7: A profile from a versatile one-piece cutter. Note guards and featherboard. This guarding is not in accordance with the regulations governing commercial use

straight and all manner of curved profiles (fig. 6.8) that you can buy off the shelf, you can also buy high-speed steel blanks with which to make your own cutters. Old mouldings like skirting board and picture rail are often impossible to match exactly, and there is an enormous sense of achievement in producing your own cutters to do the job. But it is necessary, before you get into this, to understand the machine and its capabilities in detail first; don't even begin to experiment with your own cutter shapes until you have at least a years' worth of regular (ie daily) spindle moulding experience of all kinds.

First examine the plan view of the block and cutters in fig. 6.4a, and spin it in your imagination. You will immediately see that as a straight piece of timber passes across the cutters, guided by the fences, that the cutters are not hitting the wood at right angles where they are cutting deepest, or at 'top dead centre'. Here is the key to understanding the basic principle of all spindle moulding apart from that with a French head – cutters work at a cutting angle, which is not 90°. This is because the cutters are mounted in the block tangentially, not radially. The forces they take when cutting would be far too great if they were on a line passing through the centre of the block, and they are designed to slice-cut rather than scrape-and-batter cut. French-head design differs, in that the cutters go through the centre of the shaft, and thus meet the work at 90° at top dead centre. Their grinding geometry is straightforward.

The cutting angle of all other cutters – and the ones you are most likely to want to grind for yourself – is the angle contained by a line drawn from the tip of the cutter to the block centre, and one drawn out of the flat face of the cutter. The further out of the block the cutter projects, the tighter the cutting angle, and vice versa. Now

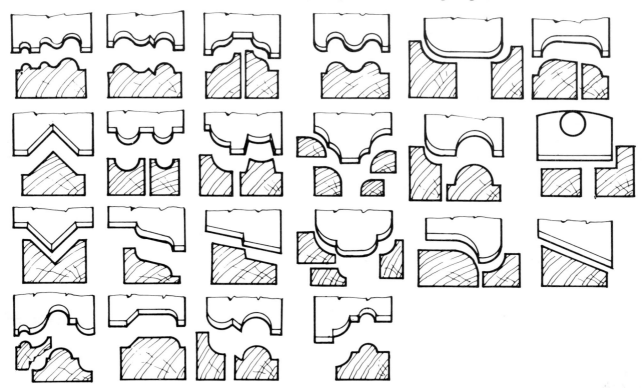

Fig. 6.8: Just a selection of cutter profiles. You can get proprietary cutters, or grind your own – but be sure you understand how

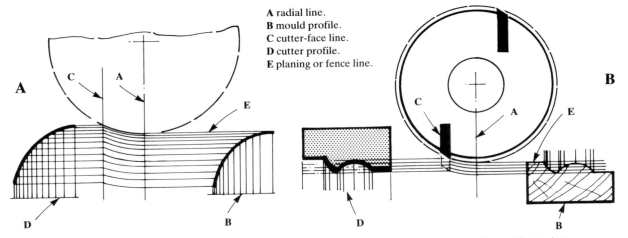

A radial line.
B mould profile.
C cutter-face line.
D cutter profile.
E planing or fence line.

Fig. 6.9A: Cutter development with a simple scale and even spacing.

Fig. 6.9B: Shows how to pick up salient points of a more complex shape

consider a cutter with a shaped profile, which at all its points will be meeting the work at different distances from the block centre, and will thus have a corresponding range of cutting angles. Just as the amount by which the cutter projects from the block is always greater than the maximum depth of cut it will achieve – because it meets the work at an angle – so also the shape of the profile you cut does not correspond exactly to the ground shape of the cutter. If it hit the work at 90°, it would be a perfect mirror-image of the profile you need, which is why French-head cutters are (comparatively) easy to grind. But it doesn't; which is why you must learn how to draw and grind a cutter shape to get the exact desired profile.

Fig. 6.9 shows you how to go about 'cutter projection'. Draw out the block and cutters full size, and draw a radial line parallel to the face of one of the cutters. Now draw the minimum cutting circle, or 'planing circle' – the minimum circumference round the block which clears any bolts or projections – and from the point where the radial line cuts the minimum cutting circle, draw a line out to the right, square to the radial line. This is the 'planing line', which represents the fence face of the machine, and the line on which the uncut face of the work will run.

Now draw out the section of your proposed moulding, working out how it should run against the fence, with the part of the moulding that touches the fence touching the 'planing line'. Now draw lines vertical to the planing line along the profile of the moulding, preferably at perfectly regular intervals, usually 2 or 4mm depending on the complexity of the curve. If it is a compound shape like the one in fig. 6.9B, lines at the points of change will do; but to get the idea, stick to a simple shape first and make your line spacing regular. Transfer those parallel lines, vertical to the planing line, to the left of your full-size block drawing, using exactly the same spacing.

Now draw lines parallel to the planing line, starting at where the vertical lines intersect with the moulding profile, going to meet the block's radial line to the left. From where they meet the radial line, draw arcs concentric to the block round to the cutter face line. Do this with a good pair of compasses. From that cutter face line, continue the lines out to the left, parallel to the planing line, so they will intersect with the vertical spacing lines you have already drawn. Now just join up the points of intersection on the left-hand side, and you have the projected cutter shape to grind.

THE SPINDLE MOULDER

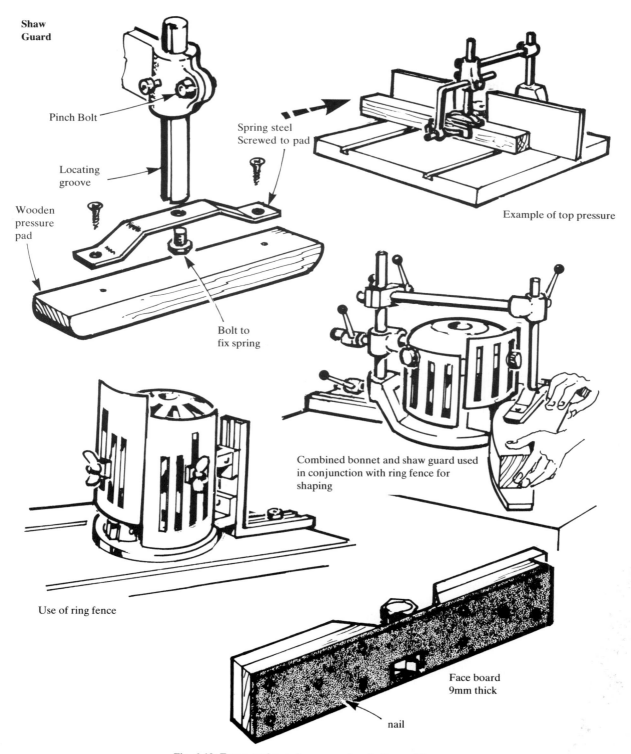

Shaw Guard

Pinch Bolt

Locating groove

Wooden pressure pad

Spring steel Screwed to pad

Bolt to fix spring

Example of top pressure

Combined bonnet and shaw guard used in conjunction with ring fence for shaping

Use of ring fence

Face board 9mm thick

nail

Fig. 6.10: Fences and guards common in spindle moulding

When you have finished, you have drawn the cutter shape to produce the profile shape you want. But remember it is specific to that block with that fence setting. If you change the block size, cutter position in the block or fences, you are changing the cutter projection and thus cutting angles, and the whole thing will be different, if only marginally. You must mount the cutters, when you have ground them, in the block in the same position as you have plotted them. If you transfer your drawing on to a piece of thin ply – or better, do it on a piece of ply from the start – you can use that as a setting template to locate the cutters in the block.

As you grind the shape – wearing goggles, of course – have a can of water next to the wheel and dip the cutter in it every few moments to keep the steel cool. Grind the shape first to match the projected profile on your grid, then relieve the back edges off the face of the cutter which first meets the work. This is again a product of cutting angle; if you left the edges at 90°, the back edge would scrape away the shape that the front one has made. Grind back at least 10° on top and bottom edges, and up to 45° on the shaped 'vertical' edges; the deeper the cutter projects into the wood, the more clearance you need.

All of which is highly technical and not a little daunting. There are indeed a huge number of ready-ground cutters you can get, and you may never need or want to grind your own; but this part of spindle moulding is intensely satisfying, and gives you an opportunity to develop and perfect a skill that is almost an art. Don't worry if your first few attempts take an age to get right; there will always be a number of test cuts and test settings to make. It is likely that you will start on grinding straight shapes for rebates and grooves; remember here too that clearance and projection are just as important to take into account. For a 15mm straight cut, for instance, you will probably need something like 17mm cutter projection. There is always trial and error, of course!

Cutter safety

For 'Whitehill' type blocks, work out how much projection you need – always have about two-thirds of the cutter gripped – and, most important, **balance the cutters in the block**. It takes care and time; you must set them up so that one edge makes exactly the same cut as the other. They must be the same size and weight, and if you're using a proprietary safety-block, use only the cutters made by the manufacturer for that block. **NEVER** use cutters which show signs of damage, wear or defect. To eliminate risks of accidents from faulty tools, some manufacturers advise that cutters are re-ground only twice, and should be discarded after a total of 60 hours' work. **CLEAN** all the gripping and gripped surfaces with meths every time you set cutters up in a block. **ALWAYS** use tools at, or below, the manufacturers' recommended speed. Most spindle moulding tasks have an optimum speed – the larger the cutting diameter, obviously, the greater the speed of the tips of the cutters. Manufacturers usually recommend maximum speeds for their blocks; don't exceed them.

Machine safety and adjustments

Cutter and block safety is only one aspect of the safe operation of a spindle moulder. As with any machine, it's vital to read the manufacturer's handbook, and to use the guards and fences provided. You'll certainly be making your own (fig. 6.10). The Shaw guard and hold-down and hold-in units (horizontal and vertical pressure-guards) should be placed to hold the workpiece and stop it kicking back. Always face the 'butterfly' fences – the two main ones either side of the shaft – with thick, stable ply so you can bring them closer together than the standard metal ones will go. The smaller the gap between the two sides, the better; in fact the Woodworking Machines Regulations 1974 recommend that you fit a face-board right across the gap whenever possible. Minimum exposure for the cutters

Fig. 6.11: Cutter height is adjusted by the hand wheel; here, a tommy-bar locks the shaft

is the rule. You can also pin stops and guides to the fences if they are ply-faced; and if cutters do contact them, you won't do nearly so much damage.

The two halves of the butterfly fence adjust independently, back and forward as well as in and out. This is important in 'planing', when the surface being fed into the machine is to be entirely cut away; the outfeed fence will have to be

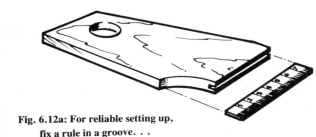

Fig. 6.12a: For reliable setting up,
fix a rule in a groove. . .

. . . in a piece of ply to measure
depth of cut off the fence . . .

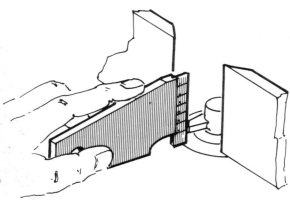

. . . and cutter height off the table

adjusted to run against the cut surface.

The height of the spindle is adjusted by turning the hand-wheel on the side of the machine below the work table (fig. 6.11). For the greatest accuracy, the spindle height should always be set on the upward movement, because the spindle and motor are being moved together, and they can settle a little on the screw-threads of the adjustment mechanism after you've locked it and turned the machine on. Always work up to a height, so you're moving the whole weight against the adjuster, and any slack is already taken up. Also, make a point of locking and unlocking the adjuster every time you alter the height – some are lazy and don't do it, which eventually means you wear out your lock and then can't hold your cutters to a height. Fig. 6.12a shows a handy little gauge you can make that helps cutter height and depth setting, and fig. 6.12b the use of a dial gauge, which is far more accurate and can work in both planes.

When you've made and checked all the adjustments to set the cut up – to cutters, guards and fences – turn the cutter by hand to see that it doesn't foul anything. Then make a habit of checking the adjustments again, preferably with a methodically numbered mental check-list; write it out on a big board and hang it up over the machine:
- Cutters firmly fixed in block?
- Block securely fixed to spindle?
- Spindle height locked?
- Spindle brake-lock off?
- All fences adjusted and tight?
- All guards and hold-downs tight enough but not too tight?

Even if you are satisfied with the setting of the machine, it could be fatal to let your attention flag as you feed the wood into it. Spindle moulders, like circular saws, can snatch and throw out lumps of wood; feed smoothly and slowly, especially at the beginning of the cut. A power feed is an ideal solution, adding safety as well as ease, speed and smoothness to the feed operation.

Fig. 6.12b: A dial guage, yet more accurate, can be used for setting height and projection

Fig. 6.13: Check your stock carefully. Close and straight grain (right) is best

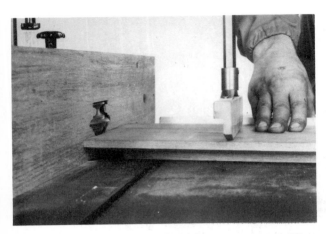

Fig. 6.14: A panel is moulded on the back; pressure-guard, sliding table and face-board are all in use. Always measure from the table

Fig. 6.15: High narrow workpieces need high fences; push-stick at the ready

The following points will help:

• Always feed against the direction of rotation. Where appropriate, clamp end-blocks in suitable positions

• Use pushsticks whenever possible; they're essential when moulding small pieces

• Always set up the work so that the cutters are underneath it if possible

• Always use longer pieces of wood than you need. The ends of mouldings are not always accurate, particularly with small sections

• Use a test piece *first*. All the machine settings are trial-and-error, and however many measuring devices you have on the set-up, you aren't

going to know the cut until you cut

• Make an anti-kickback device by cutting long, angled 'teeth' into a piece of plywood. Clamp it on to the worktable, hard against the workpiece which is against the fence, and test that you can push the work through but not pull it back. This is known as a feather-board (fig. 6.4)

• If you have some really big rebates to do, consider cutting them out with a saw, and only using the spindle moulder to clean up and get the exact size. This is just as quick, easier to set up, and you end up with useful fillet-sized pieces as offcuts rather than a whole bagful of shavings

• Beware of curved, twisted or split timber. Unless you have a really heavy power-feed – and often not even then – the accuracy of your cut will be seriously undermined by badly prepared wood (fig. 6.13)

• Use common sense when you're thinking of machining small-section pieces, especially brittle hardwoods like oak. Cutters spinning round in a heavy block have an enormous inertia, and there is a minimum size you can safely put through a spindle moulder – depending, of course, on the size of cutter and size of cut. In the same way, power-feeds can distort small-section timber, so you might have to use a router, or even a scratch-stock

• When planning a cornice or a moulding that will sit high up, judge how it will look at a height rather than at eye level. If you build up a moulding in several passes, make the *shallowest cut first* so that you have always got the widest edges running against fences and table. With cutters buried in the wood, this isn't always possible; often you find yourself working with the workpiece upside down.

Now you're set up, ready for ordinary straight cuts. Here are some suggestions for other operations.

Edge work on panels

Always check that the panels are flat and work

Fig. 6.16: Fixing the all-important face-board over the gap for small work

to a surface you know is square and true; with the datum face on the work-table, measure from the table. Man-made boards can vary in thickness! Once the machine setting and checking is complete, rebates, grooves and slots are easy. You can get extension tables for most machines to support larger workpieces, but even so, they will need careful handling. Make sure the hold-downs are near enough the cutter to keep the cut constant, but support for a large panel towards its outside edge is also necessary (fig. 6.14).

Small, thin, or tall workpieces

Make a false fence or face-board and secure it to the fences, across the gap. Make the opening as small as possible; short or thin pieces of wood

Fig. 6.17: Tenoning with the workpiece firmly held and a back-up block against break-out

Fig. 6.18: Dropped-in cuts should be carefully set up; *always have a backstop*

can get drawn into the machine as they pass the end of the fence. Tall pieces obviously need tall fences (fig. 6.15), and you'll need to work out ways of holding them properly vertical as well. It's quite likely that you'll be making up your own versions of pressure-guards and hold-downs for non-standard jobs.

When you fit a face-board (fig. 6.10), have a care. Say you're slotting the narrow end of a board for a tongue; the cutter height can be preset, but the depth setting will have to allow for the face-board. Set the cutters to the required height, then bring the fences forward away from them and lock them parallel. Fix the face-board firmly across them – screwing them is best in this case – and then start the machine and tap a long, stout block of wood held across the top of the face of both fences so that fences and face-board move back into the spinning cutters. It goes without saying you should be wearing eye-protection. You have to judge when the cutters are pushing through the faceboard to the depth you need.

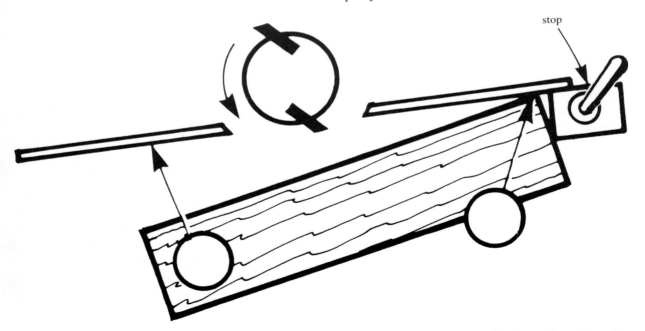

Fig. 6.19: Dropping in. The work must be positioned firmly against stop and fence before it is moved against the rotating cutter; only when there is absolutely no possibility of the workpiece being kicked in the direction of the cutter rotation should it be brought smoothly into contact with the cutter

Fig. 6.20: An unguarded ring-fence. The mark is where the cut will be deepest when the cutter is adjusted

Another and rather hairier way of getting this set-up is to set the height of the cutter and the depth of cut with the fences, allowing for the thickness of the face-board. Then pin a backstop the height of the face-board to the infeed (back) fence, and hold the face-board firmly on the table with your forearms braced. With the back end held firmly against the b⁻ckstop, slowly pivot the front end towards anc against the outfeed fence with the cutters spinning (fig. 6.16). The point is that the cutters have to make their own hole for the minimum gap – and maximum effect – of the face-board. It follows that you should use stout and evengrained timber for the face-board (½in/12mm minimum) because it takes quite a thump as you feed it into the cutters. Be careful, smooth, slow and confident. If you don't feel confident, you'll have to try and

jigsaw the right size-and-shape hole out of the face-board, but this is awkward because the cutting circle means that the hole is a different shape one side of the board from the other.

Cutting and moulding across the grain

Not often called for; but when raising and fielding panels, it's best to cut the short, cross-grained section first so that any break-out at the edges will be removed by the second cut along the grain (fig. 6.14). Otherwise, back up the cross-grained cut with a piece of scrap to stop break-out.

Tenoning

You can use a single block, where the wood

passes right over the cutters, and turn it over; or double-block arrangements, spaced apart the thickness of the tenon, are very efficient. With a single block, the distance between the table and the top of the cutters is critical, as this will be the depth of the tenon's shoulder. Remember your top and bottom edges are cutting the cheeks of the tenon – they need cutting-edge clearance as well as the vertical edges. This again is cross-grained cutting, so you need a hefty false fence on the sliding fence to back the cut up and stop break-out (fig. 6.17). Make sure the clamping is good – holding the workpiece by hand against the sliding fence is not enough. Sliding tables are available for most machines, an excellent accessory for tenoning.

Dropped-in work

Grooves and rebates often have to be stopped and started before the beginning or end – or both – of furniture and joinery components. The circle made by the cutters obviously means that such cuts will not have square ends (fig. 6.18), but these can be chiselled out later if necessary. The grooves in window sashes, for instance, for the sash cords, don't even need that.

Stopped or 'dropped-in' work is easy enough

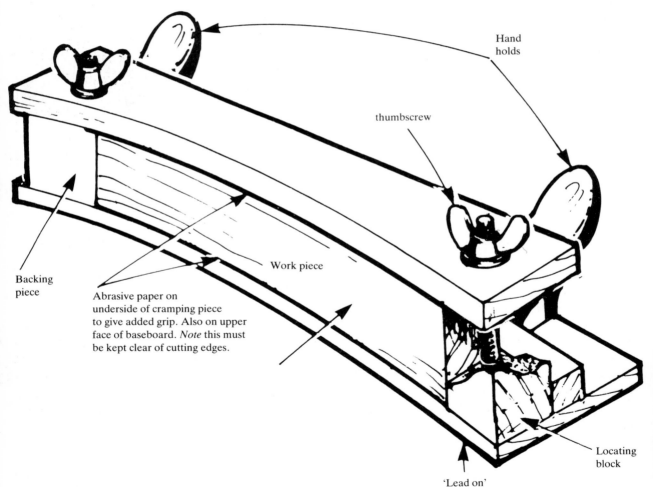

Hand holds

thumbscrew

Backing piece

Abrasive paper on underside of cramping piece to give added grip. Also on upper face of baseboard. *Note* this must be kept clear of cutting edges.

Work piece

Locating block

'Lead on'

Fig. 6.21: A typical jig for a curved shape of straight section. This could run off same-size bearing-guides or a ring-fence

Fig. 6.22: A rebate cut with a bearing guide on top of the block; the work itself runs against the guide

on the spindle moulder as long as you take great care and set up your fences and guards properly. The principle is, as always, to feed the workpiece against the rotation of the cutters; set up a backstop to hold the rear end and stop the work from being snatched and thrown backwards (fig. 6.19). Naturally your hold-downs and pressure-guards are all in place.

Screw a hefty lump of wood to the infeed fence, in a position that puts the cutters to the work where the cut starts. Careful marking and calculating is needed in these preliminary stages. Once you are sure you have everything right do a test cut; start the machine and push the workpiece slowly and firmly under the guards and up against the fence so that the cutters are at full depth. Only when the cut is at full depth and the work hard against the fence should you move the wood forward along the outfeed fence. A holding jig is the best way of making sure that the cut is smooth and your hands safe; small pieces can be put on a jig, or a board with handles and pins can be used for larger ones. If the cut is stopped at both ends, fix a forward stop on the outfeed fence to set the right place to finish the cut. If it's a very deep cut, set up to do it in two goes; do all your pieces at half depth, then set full depth and do them all again.

Curved work

There are two main ways to approach curved grooving, rebating and moulding – doing such work on curved pieces, that is; they involve

Fig. 6.23: A stout infeed finger, a bonnet-guard and a top bearing

guide-bearings on the block itself or a 'ring-fence' (fig. 6.20). The other major decision to make is whether or not to use a jig (fig. 6.21). If your workpiece has a constant, well-produced profile, it's possible to use a block with a guide-bearing and the edge of the piece itself as a guide against which the guide-bearing runs (fig. 6.22). This is where you are limited to the range of guides that come with the block, which will only allow you to get certain depths of rebate corresponding to the difference between cutting diameter and guide diameter. With a jig the exact finished shape of the component, you can use a guide the same size as the block to get the perfect shape of a roughly-sawn workpiece. Rebates and moulds on that piece, however, will

involve a different guide-bearing or a ring-fence.

Before you do any curved work at all, fix up an infeed finger (fig. 6.23). There's only one point where you get maximum depth of cut, because you're presenting a wide-radius piece to a much smaller cutting diameter, so you must be exceptionally careful about feeding the work into the cut smoothly. The infeed finger is set up so you cannot dig the work in at full depth straight away; it comes in gradually. Cut a long shallow curve of stout ply and clamp it securely to the worktable so you can slide the work easily and safely into the cutter; the point of the finger should nearly touch the cutters. Always feed the wood against the rotation of the cutters; if you need to take another bite, which is quite likely since you won't get full depth at the first pass, **never move the wood backwards** on the cutters. Pull it away, and feed it in again, always against the direction of rotation.

The ring-fence gives you more flexibility than a rebate block with guide-bearings. You can use any moulding cutter with it, and set up (within reason) almost any depth of cut; if you have a really deep cut to make, it's best to set up in two goes so you never ask the cutters to go too deep in one go. The ring-fence, usually used with a 'bonnet-guard' that looks something like a helmet (fig. 6.10), is not a perfect circle, but slightly oval-shaped, so it does the job of an infeed finger. There is a mark on the ring itself which shows where maximum depth of cut comes. The

advantage of this device is that you can use the same jig to produce the shape, rebate it and mould it (fig. 6.24) – as you'll need to do, for instance, on a curved-top panelled door; your jig should be made with extreme precision and plenty of extra material at either end of the workpiece to fix the piece firmly on to it and leave room for your hands, and preferably jig-clamps as well. These are like mini-holdfasts which you screw to the jig, and they act as handles as well, keeping your hands well out of the way. Have the jig on top of the workpiece and the cutters buried if possible, but it isn't always, because you will probably want to re-bate one side of the piece and mould the other. For this sort of work, components should always be made oversize so you can pin or fix to the jig

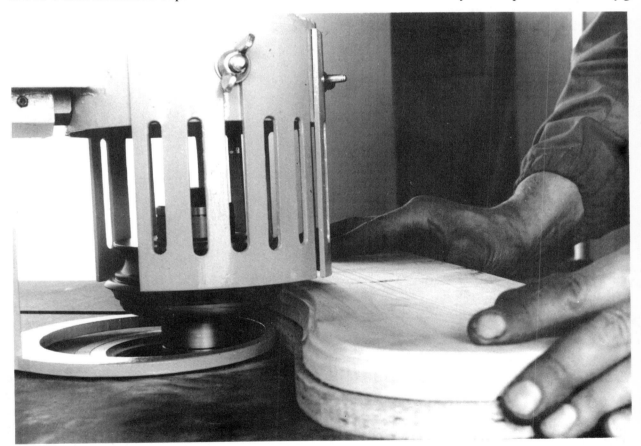

Fig. 6.24: Ring-fence against jig produces a mould on top

through waste, and then cut to the correct size when your spindle moulding is all done; curved pieces also have awkward cross grain as well, which it's best to leave in waste areas so you can discard broken bits.

You won't get very far in curved spindle mouldings if you don't get to grips with jigs. Remember your components are exact reproductions of the shape of the jig, so absolute precision is vital. It also pays to remember that you'll be doing several setups and trial-and-errors, so make a few extra components to start with as test pieces. Another aspect of testing on scrap, of course, is that with a curved or ring-fence you can cut a simple rebate on a straight piece to exactly the same depth as you can on a curved piece, so you can use ordinary scrap initially. When you get to moulding, of course, it's a different matter.

Angled cuts

Dovetail grooves, glazing rebates with angled sides or bottoms, or indeed any cut that requires to be made at an angle to the square edges of the workpiece needs to be thought out carefully. Put a cutter in the block at an angle? It won't work. Imagine a square cutter set in a stationary block with a corner pointing down at the table. Now turn the block round in your mind. The lowest point of the cutter makes the complete circle at that lowest point – it would cut out a flat. So you need to make up an angled jig set against the fence, clamped and screwed, that will present the work at an angle to the knives; or you can use a tilting spindle, if you are lucky enough to have a machine with one. This, incidentally, is why you should set a cutter at a very slight angle to give a flat-bottomed or topped cut; the finish is cleaner.

Dust extraction

It's almost impossible to extract curved-work waste from a spindle moulder because the workpieces move all over the table. For straight work, extraction is a legal imperative. Most fences include an extraction hood which doubles as a cutter guard; you can build your own out of thick ply to take your extraction system.

CHAPTER 7

THE MORTISER

The mortise and tenon is the standard joint of quality woodwork, especially door- and window-frames (joinery) and furniture. It is strong, attractive and easy to make with the right tools (and machinery), and the right insistence on accuracy. Tenons can be cut in all sorts of different ways on a variety of machines, but machine-made mortises are best and quickest with either a specific machine or an attachment to a universal machine or planer/thicknesser.

There are two principal methods of making mortises by machine; hollow-chisel and slotting. The first uses a hollow, square chisel, wider at its cutting end than at the shank, inside which a drill (an auger, as it's known) rotates. With the free-standing hollow-chisel mortiser, the tool is pulled down towards the workpiece by a hand-operated lever (fig. 7.1). As it enters the wood, the auger cuts a hole first and the chisel follows through, squaring off the corner.

Principles – hollow chisels

It's essential that the auger enters the wood first. There's no way the chisel alone could penetrate the workpiece to any great depth, far less remove the internal section of the mortise. The chisel's work is to square off the initial round hole made by the auger, and consequently, the

Fig. 7.1: The hollow-chisel mortiser

shape of the machine chisel with its four promi-nent sharp cornerpoints bears no resemblance to the flat face of the hand-tool.

To ensure the auger cuts first, before the chisel, the cutting edges ('ears') of the auger bit should be set 0.3mm below the cornerpoints of the chisel for chisel up to 12.7mm (½in), and 1.6mm below the chisel points for chisels larger than that (fig. 7.2). It's often tricky to get this exactly right, but a good 'rule of thumb' that old-time joiners used was to set the auger ears below the chisel points the thickness of an old penny, which is of course, considerably more than 0.3mm. If you get the auger too far away from the chisel, you'll both reduce the effectiveness of the chisel and end up with a mortise with a 'stepped' finish on the bottom of the cut; if you set the auger too close up into the chisel, both will overheat and blunt, and the auger might break off. It will certainly damage the steel of both auger and chisel.

The auger bit is also specially designed. It has no central screw-point like the augers for car-penter's braces, because the bottom of the cut needs a flat finish. It would also make it difficult to control the feed-speed and withdraw the bit from the wood. The auger's two cutting wings – 'ears' – on its outer edges cut slightly wider than the diameter of the auger body. The ears make the hole larger than the upper shank of the chisel, which also tapers; otherwise the tool would wedge in the workpiece.

The hollow chisel has a 'window' running most of its length; this is so the waste chips will be thrown out during mortising by the spiral ac-tion of the auger. It's obviously vital that you set the chisel into the machine with the window to the side so the waste can come out into the holes you've already drilled. If the window is to the face of the mortise, the chips will jam up inside the chisel, overheat, and possibly distort both steel and wood. It's worth mentioning that *cool-ing* is a bugbear of mortising – keep it in mind as you set up.

Fig. 7.2: Set the auger just below the chisel; too far in or out can mean disaster

Principles – slot mortising

In the slotting method, the workpiece, mounted on a sliding table, is moved towards the revolving cutter (fig. 7.3). For the machines with which we are concerned, the cutter revolves in a set position and the workpiece moves.

The best type of horizontal mortising cutter for hand-fed machines is the 'double-edged slot-mortiser cutter' (fig. 7.4), which is basically a drill with two full-length cutting edges – not unlike a router cutter – and edges on the bottom diameter which finish the bottom of the cut. You push the workpiece into the cutters and move it from side to side with the cut at the same depth before making a second plunge cut. There are other kinds of horizontal slot-mortise cutters (fig. 7.4b shows a chair-mortise bit for industrial

applications), but whichever ones you use, always remember that different bits require different procedures, so follow the manufacturer's instructions carefully. Most double-edged cutters these days have serrations on the body, which mesh up the chips and aid waste removal – not a natural process as it is with the auger and chisel.

Hollow-chisel mortising

Setting up

The adjustments on the hollow-chisel mortiser are to the height and back-to-front position of the sliding table (fig. 7.5), and to the height at which the downward movement of the chisel stops. The clamping arrangement by which the

Fig. 7.3: A horizontal slot-mortiser on a planer/thicknesser. This version is operated with one lever

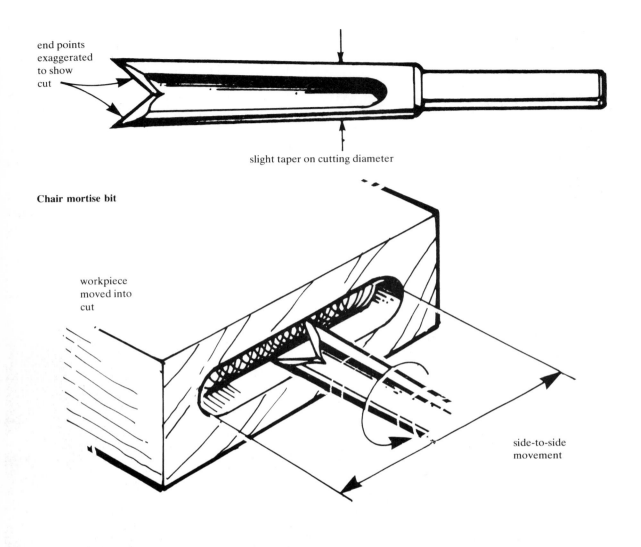

end points
exaggerated
to show
cut

slight taper on cutting diameter

Chair mortise bit

workpiece
moved into
cut

side-to-side
movement

A Double-edged slot-mortise cutter with serrated edges

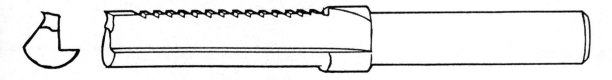

Fig 7.4: Types of horizontal slot-mortise bit

workpiece is held on to the table usually slides back and forth to accommodate wide/thick pieces, but there is a screw-up or cam-locking action on this which will work for pieces within a common width range, without having to reposition the whole mechanism. This clamping block normally comes just with a round square pad, so you must attach a solid, larger lump of wood to it to extend the clamping pressure along the length of the workpiece, and also stop the work bruising. Don't make the extra pressure-pad too thick, or you'll use up the adjustment range of the block.

It's quite fiddly to set the chisel and auger up correctly, but it must be done meticulously because you risk broken, bent or burnt augers and chisels. Fig. 7.6 shows the various chisel parts of a hollow-chisel machine. There is a bush to fit into the body of the moving part of the mortiser, which will carry the round neck of the square chisel. Into and up through this goes the auger, which is held in the machine by (usually) a grub-screw that tightens through a revolving collet on to a flat on the auget (fig. 7.7). It's **absolutely essential** that you get the grub-screw tightened up on this flat; if it doesn't locate on the flat it won't hold the auger in the correct vertical position, and the auger will travel up into the chisel under working pressure. Result: burnt and blunt auger (probably broken), burnt and de-tempered chisel (probably cracked into the bargain). At around £20 a time for chisel, auger and collar, getting this right is worth it!

Hand-tighten the collar and chisel, held by a

Fig. 7.5: The upper wheel moves the table side to side; the lower one moves it in and out

separate clamping action of the machine's split neck, while you sort the auger out; there's often no way of stopping the various bits and pieces move round in relation to each other, so the best way is to keep the auger in one position as you move it up, lining the grub screw-up with one of the auger ears at the bottom.

Once you're satisfied the auger is right and at the right height in relation to the chisel, of course (which is why you hand-tightened the chisel at the correct height), you must square up the chisel precisely to the fence. This is easiest done by moving the table out towards you until it's a hair's breadth away from the chisel. Back-and-forth movement of the table is either by a wheel separate from the side-to-side one, or on some machines you pull the wheel outwards to engage in another set of gears (fig. 7.5). **DON'T TOUCH THE CHISEL WITH THE FENCE!** You'll bend or break the chisel. Get it so you can just see light between it and the metal face of the fence, and adjust it square so there's exactly the same hair's-breadth distance either side of the chisel between it and the fence.

Most hollow-chisel mortisers don't lend themselves to stops for side-to-side movement to regulate the length of your mortise, because you're usually mortising both ends of a piece, and the stops would be in different relationship to each other for different mortise positions. If you have a run of constant-position mortises to do, it could be worth setting up limiters to regulate the movement of the table, but it means you must put each workpiece in exactly the same position on the table. Even for long runs, it's usually easier to mark the ends of the mortises on the workpieces themselves; their position in relation to the thickness of the piece is of course decided by the back-and-forth movement of the table. The standard habit of clamping a number of stiles to be mortised together and marking them all out with sets of lines squared across them is of course the answer here. You just don't have to bother marking mortise width and location in the workpiece thickness, because once you've set the machine up, that's all taken care of.

The final adjustment is to the height of the

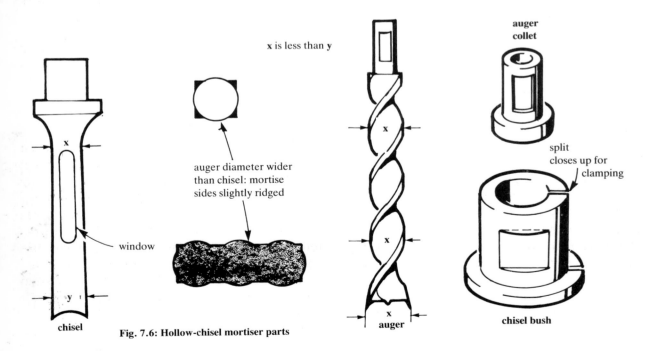

x is less than y

auger diameter wider than chisel: mortise sides slightly ridged

window

chisel

auger collet

split closes up for clamping

chisel bush

auger

Fig. 7.6: Hollow-chisel mortiser parts

Fig. 7.7: An allen-key tightens the grub-screw for a positive hold on the auger; the chisel is perfectly square to the fence

chisel's stopping-point, which obviously means the depth of your mortise (fig. 7.8). You can make a mark on a workpiece, adjust the table away so the chisel misses it completely, and bring the arm down so the chisel stops at the mark. Most machines have enough stiffness in the action for the chisel to stay where it is while you adjust the depth stop – usually just a moveable block on a fixed vertical rod which bears on to a ledge on the stationary part of the machine. If you're doing stepped mortises, or, far more common, haunches out to the ends of a stile (fig. 7.9), there might be a dual-stop arrangement, or it's often easier just to cut a little hardwood block equal to the distance between the bottom of the mortise and the bottom of the cut for the haunch. In other words, if your mortise stops 10mm from the table and your haunch

stops 45mm from it, you need a 35mm-thick block. Chop the mortise, then slip the block in under the stop and you effectively raise the height of the stop.

Running

When you're set up, test on scrap as always. Check that the line of the mortise stays parallel with the work, check the auger isn't moving up into the chisel, check the depth you're getting – generally a mortise (if it isn't a through one) should be 3-5mm deeper than the length of the tenon. As you go through the work, make sure you keep all your face marks to the fence for accuracy and consistency. This is of course even more important if your mortises are offset, not centred on the workpiece thickness.

You should have a wooden block of consistent

thickness below the workpiece, to stop any possible disasters involving unwitting attempts to cut mortises in a solid steel table. It should naturally be thinner than the width of the workpiece, or the clamp will work on the false bedding-piece and not the workpiece. This is essential if you're doing through-mortises, for which you're unlikely to have a depth-stop set up (though this isn't a bad idea for safety). Don't cut all the way through from one side for through-mortises; mark the lines all the way round the workpieces, cut halfway one side and the other half the other. Nasty breakout can occur if you try to go all the way through from one side. If you're doing wedged through-tenons, when you turn the piece over (keeping the same face-side to the fences of course), bring the chisel down fractionally beyond the line rather than just on it or just

inside it, as you have done for the tenon-shoulder side. This will widen the mortise somewhat at the back edge, and allow for the expansion that the wedges will cause.

Remember – when you're designing something with mortise and tenon joints, decide what width of mortise you're going to use very early on. Apart from the fact that it's easier to fit a tenon to a mortise than the other way round, it will affect your decisions about rebates and grooves. You should be able to match the width of grooves to the mortise-widths, so when you groove after first mortising then tenoning, the grooves in the stiles give you the right depth for the haunch to sit into and those in the rails define the exact width of the tenon.

Mortise thickness is based on approximately a third of workpiece thickness, and obviously re-

Fig. 7.8: Measuring for mortise depth. If height allows, block the work up on the table

Fig. 7.9: A haunching cut finishes a stile-end mortise. Note the vertical depth-stop bar

lates to the standard available chisel sizes. It's possible but a pain to make mortises wider than standard-size chisels (imperial or metric), because it involves resetting the back-to-front movement of the table, either at every mortise or after a run which must then be repeated. Also, be sure to clamp the work near the pressure-pad, but not right between it and the fence, because it will exert undue pressure on the area where the chisel is operating.

Finally, make sure you always chop your square holes at both ends of the mortise first, so you can get accurately to the lines, then clear away the waste in between. This is because the chisel will deflect slightly if it's half on and half off wood to be cut, and the ends of the mortise won't be vertical. DON'T TRAVERSE THE CHISEL FROM SIDE TO SIDE IN THE CUT AS IT CUTS! This is the sure way to bent and broken chisels.

Horizontal slot-mortising

Setting up

To all intents and purposes, the tables that fit on universal machines for slot-mortising are much the same as the ones that go on to planer/thicknessers. The bit is usually mounted in a chuck which fits on the outboard end of the cutter-block shaft, which means that the speed of cutter-rotation is much higher (between 5000 and 10,000rpm) than on hollow-chisel machines. You are also biting into wood and then moving it back and forth across the spinning cut-

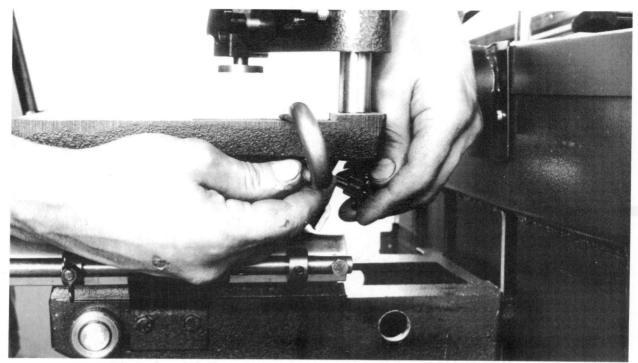

Fig. 7.10: Various stops are operated by collars, knobs and nuts. Here the end-stop for the workpiece is adjusted

Fig. 7.11: Table-height adjustment (in this case) is by a handle connected to the machine's thicknessing table

ter, so you need an understanding of what you're asking a cutter to do, and thus a sympathy. This amounts to: **don't** bite too deep in one go, and **don't** traverse the table too fast.

The adjustments on this type of machine regulate where you will put the work (end-stop clamps, fig. 7.10); the position of the mortise in relation to the thickness of the workpiece (table height, fig. 7.11); the length of the mortise (side-to-side table travel): and mortise depth (back-to-front table travel). Various machines do all these in various ways, but if you're buying, it obviously makes sense to examine closely the ease of use and potential accuracy of these stops and clamps. It's often quoted as a difficulty with horizontal mortising arrangements that although there's a stop for the side-to-side movement of the table, there's no end-stop for

the position of the workpiece on the table. Some do have this, some don't; but if there isn't a facility for keeping the position of a succession of workpieces constant to the table, obviously stops to regulate the side-to-side movements of the table are little use.

So you'll have to make your own, and it could hardly be simpler. Just clamp a block on to one end of the sliding table, and make sure the workpieces are always hard up against that. There is usually a low lip or fence on the table to keep the workpiece parallel along its length to the travel of the table. The constancy of position of the workpiece (and mortise) in relation to that end-stop block clamped to the table, of course, depends entirely on the unvarying lengths of the workpieces. It won't work if they're all different lengths!

Fig. 7.12: A horizontal slot-mortise: square the hole or round the peg?

Running

When all the adjustments are made, run tests on scrap as usual. The in-and-out and side-to-side action of the horizontal mortiser demands a bit of concentration at first to get the right co-ordination; it's a bit like the 'pat head, rub tummy' trick. The most important thing is not to bite too deep before you go side-to-side. Start the cut, as you would with a hollow-chisel machine, by drilling to full depth at both ends, then work between the two spaces. Bite in about ¼in/6mm, cut across, then take another small bite and cut back the other way. It's better while you're unused to the action to underestimate the depth you can go rather than overestimate. If you get chatter and vibration, it's obvious you're asking the machine to do too much.

Cutter size, strength and sharpness, speed of rotation, the hardness of the wood, and numerous other factors all affect how deep you can go and how fast; some machines have one lever for both axes of table-travel, others have two, which are a little harder to co-ordinate.

Horizontal slot-mortises have round ends (fig. 7.12), which will mean either that you round off the corners of your tenons with chisel, rasp and file, or that you square up the mortises themselves with a chisel. One particular advantage of horizontal mortisers is that you can cut mortises in the edges of much wider workpieces than a hollow-chisel mortiser will take. The limits of table height and chisel height of a hollow-chisel type usually stop you making satisfactory mortises in, for instance, rails deeper than about 10in, while as long as you've got the work properly supported on a horizontal table, you could slot-mortise a 24in board if you felt the need.

Sharpening

It's vital to keep both augers and hollow chisels, and the cutting edges of double-edged slot cutters, as keen as a razor. Blunt edges heat themselves and the wood, and mortises are not air-cooled like most machined surfaces. For an

Sharpening a hollow chisel

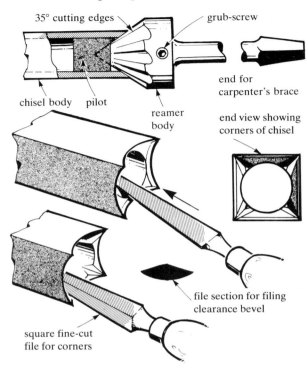

Sharpening an auger

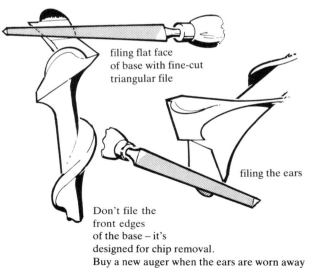

Fig. 7.13

auger and chisel, you need a selection of fine files and a conical reamer or grinder (fig. 7.13). The ears and flat bottom face of the auger should be dressed every time you set it up, and the four points of the hollow chisel should be of equal length and equal sharpness. When there's nothing left of an auger's ears, bin it.

The reamer, which fits in a carpenter's brace, is a common workshop accessory for hollow-chisel users. It comes with a selection of pilot pieces which fit the internal diameter of the chisel, and guide the ground edges of the reamer (which looks something like a countersink) on to the edges and corners equally. Dress the outside flat faces of the chisels, after you've reamed on the inside, using a fine oil- or water-stone to remove the burr. The long edges of double-edged slot cutters should also be dressed, but proper sharpening is best done by experts with sophisticated machinery – especially if your cutters are tungsten-edged.

CHAPTER 8

SANDING

Don't ever let anyone tell you that sanding by machine is a complete substitute for sanding by hand. By sanding, of course, we really mean 'abrading', because even average standards of finish on furniture are best achieved with garnet and silicone papers, not the familiar 'sandpaper' (which is in fact glasspaper). Hand sanding is hard, boring work, but it is satisfying. The virtue of patience is rewarded as you watch and feel the wood responding to your hands (or block), coming up smooth and silky, with a warmth that only hand-work seems to give.

But there's no hyperbole to get you round the fact it's a chore; which is why there are sanding

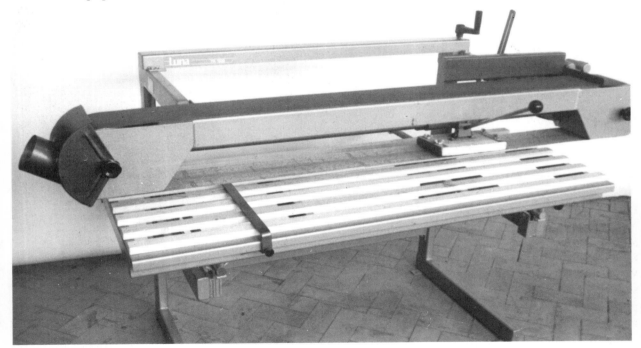

Fig. 8.1: A 6ft sliding-table belt sander. Note enclosed drums and the captive pad on the bar; the fence for top sanding is at the right-hand end, dust extraction outlet at the extreme left, and table-height adjuster on the top at the right

Fig. 8.2: Flat sanding on a small drum/belt combination machine. The vertical fence turns round to act as a table

machines. We aren't looking at rotary discs on power drills here, or even the hand-held belt sanders, much more powerful and capable of getting a far finer finish. We are looking at workshop-size machines, and featured here are two versatile versions of standard models; the sliding-table belt sander (fig. 8.1), and a drum-and-belt combination (fig. 8.2). A small stationary belt sander (12-18in useable length) is often called a linisher. Look at catalogues and manufacturers' ranges for the wide variety of types – they will almost certainly be disc, belt, drum or a

combination of any or all. The huge automatic-feed 'wide belt' (36in) sanders also need not concern us here; they are very expensive, for volume production or a large professional workshop.

Abrasives

You must know your tools before you start working with them, and the abrasive belts and discs that sanding machines use are as important as are cutters to a router. Not quite as expensive, perhaps, but certainly a serious investment. Most machines use aluminium oxide grit material, with a strong cloth or paper backing; for belt sanders, be careful to mount the belts the right way round (indicated by arrows) because the seam is joined diagonally across the belt, and you can rip it apart as soon as it touches your work if you've got it wrong. The abrasives (open- or closed-coat) come in stepped grades from 80-grit (particles per sq cm) up to 320-grit or more, but the most useful workshop range is 100 (really coarse), 150 (medium finishing) and 240 (fine). Use open coat papers for resinous timbers, old finishes and paint.

With the long belts for sliding-table machines (the one in fig. 8.1 has a 6ft table), it's important to remember that atmosphere has an effect on shape. Never leave the machine with the tension on the belt, or it will curve across the width; this is not disastrous if it curves towards the worktable, but sometimes damp can make the edges curve down and the middle up, and you can very easily dig a sharp, high-speed edge into your precious work. Keeping the workshop warm and dry is always a good idea, of course, and this will minimise the problem, but that's not always possible so it's best to take the precaution of slacking off the tension at the end of every day. The edges are tough, like the rest of the belt, but even the slightest nick or tear in the edge will turn into a great rip under working loads, and the belt will shear, fly off the wheels and flap round the workshop, if it hasn't already wrapped itself round your head. So store and handle the rolled belts very carefully. A new 150-grit cloth-backed belt for a 6ft sliding-table

Fig. 8.3: Drum sanding on a spindle moulder; the drum over which the abrasive sleeve fits has a soft rubber surface

Fig. 8.4: Another version of a drum, this time a hard one on a combined drum/belt machine

Fig. 8.5: Slipping a new belt over the adjustable, undriven wheel of a sliding-table machine. Left hand holds the tension lever

Fig. 8.6: Sliding-table tracking adjustment; the spanner moves the plunger which aligns the wheel's axle

sander can cost the best part of £10! Make these tough abrasives – belts, discs, pads, sheets, whatever form they come in – last longer by de-clogging them occasionally with a wire brush. This works well when you're using resinous timber like pitch pine, but it can obviously only be done so often before renewal. Don't hold the wire brush against a belt or disc running under power, obviously – apart from safety considerations, you will find your wire-brush bristles no match for aluminium oxide at high speed.

Drum sanding

One of the simplest routes to machine sanding is to fit a sanding drum attachment on to a spindle moulder in place of the cutter-block (fig. 8.3). The 3 or 6in-diameter drum, which will be rubber-faced or even inflatable to take 6in-deep (average) tubes of abrasive paper, is ideal for curved workpieces, which should be fed through freehand and *carefully*. Several passes are often needed to get the right finish. The sanding drum attachment on a spindle moulder can also be used for flat surfaces with the two halves of the guide fence lined up to support the workpiece. This vertical drum also comes as part of a 'disc-and-bobbin' sander, where the same motor drives a large disc on one side and an 8in-high (approx.) 4in-diameter abrasive cylinder on the other. The bobbin rises and falls to spread wear on the abrasive. Fig. 8.4 shows the drum in use at the end of the combination drum/belt machine whose flat belt you can see in use in fig. 8.2. This particular machine's attraction is the adjustability through 90° of tables and abrasive surfaces. The key to successful drum or bobbin sanding is smooth feeding-in towards the rotating drum, *always against the direction of rotation*. Danger doesn't lie so much in cutting your fingers to pieces – although you can do a great deal of damage to flesh in a very short time with high-speed abrasives – as in the drum snatching the work out of your hands and spinning it off the table – in the case of the spindle moulder, at a particularly uncomfortable height. Hold the work firmly down to the table,

hands either end well away from the drum, and bring it in smoothly, walking round the machine with the curve.

Although you can get excellent results on a drum (independent, bobbin, or mounted on a spindle moulder), its usefulness is limited because 'sandable depth' is restricted by the height of the shaft and some workpieces are just too large or too awkward to handle on a small worktable.

Table belt sanding

So what most small workshops really need is a sliding-table belt sander – or 'pad sander', which comes in a variety of types and sizes. Some have

Fig. 8.7: Adjusting height on the same 6ft sliding-table. Some machines have an electric motor for this

a wide range of height adjustment on the table, some have two positions, some are designed so the table and/or the belt can turn through 90° for edge sanding. All operate on the same principle of a long, continuous abrasive belt running horizontally round two wide wheels or drums, one of which is connected to a motor. The driven wheel has a fixed position on the machine, the idler wheel is adjustable to control the tracking and tension of the belt. Between the wheel/drums, in the space between upper and lower belt positions, a captive pressure-pad slides back and forth on a fixed horizontal bat, moving up and down to press the belt on to the work. The drum-and-belt assembly is mounted over the table,

Fig. 8.8: Adjust belt height at between 5–10mm above the work

Fig. 8.9: Keep the table moving back and forth and the pad going from side to side. Make sure the stop on the table is the right height for thin pieces

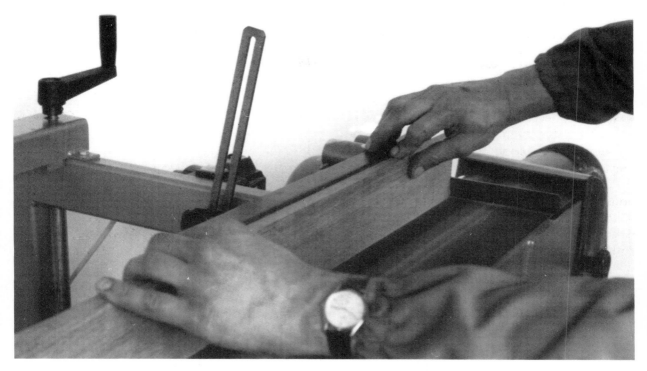

Fig. 8.10: Edge sanding on the top run of a long sliding-table belt, end of workpiece hard against the stop

Fig. 8.11: Another version of edge sanding, this time on a large sliding-table machine with the belt/drums turned through 90°

which as well as adjusting vertically, also slides backwards and forwards (ie across the long axis of the machine) beneath the belt. For situations where the mounted pad is difficult to use, you should also have a hand-held pad, a 6x10in ply block with a comfortable handle and a ¼in felt base.

All the adjustments to the belt are made on the idler drum. To load a belt, make sure the machine is off and isolated, then slacken off the drum-to-drum length and slip the belt on at both ends (fig. 8.5: make sure it's the right way round!). Then tighten the tension until downward pressure of your hand meets with a springy resistance that stops your downward movement about a hand's breadth below the straight and level. Tension is important – too tight and you'll ruin the belt and the machine's bearings, too loose and it'll flap and tear. Atmosphere, age and condition of belt, size and hardness of work – all these and other things affect your decision on how tight the belt will be. Belts stretch, obviously; check and renew settings every day. When you're satisfied the tension is right, check the tracking very carefully. The last thing you want is the belt creeping across the drums and carving a groove in the metal of the drum housings until it can take no more and has to tear. Making sure the machine is isolated, give the belt a manual turn with a wide sweep of your arm so it spins, at least momentarily, at something like operating speed. See which way it creeps across the drum, and make minute adjustments accordingly, waiting for the effect of the wheel's altered position to show up (fig. 8.6). Little by little is best – it's too easy to make too big a difference, so the belt then starts going off the drum the other side. When you reckon everything is as it should be, turn the machine very quickly on-off and you'll get an idea of how accurate your 'manual' estimate has been.

Put the work on the table and adjust the height (fig. 8.7) so the belt is 5-10mm (about ½in) above it (fig. 8.8). There should be a restraining bar across the table (fig. 8.9), whose position has to be adjusted according to the length of the workpiece; also beware very thin pieces of ply, hardboard and so on, being snatched off the table, shooting over the bar and into the other end of the shop. Thin pieces are best held on a separate board with a wooden batten across it (pins out of the belt's way) so you can sand the batten to the exact thickness of the work.

Sanding wide panels calls for good coordination, because these machines are so powerful that surfaces quickly become uneven if the pressure-pad stays in one place for more than a moment. You can soon remove a veneer completely! The secret is to *keep pressure pad and table moving continually*, the pressure pad sliding from left to right along the fixed bar and the table sliding backwards and forwards (fig. 8.9). Rather the same 'pat head, rub tummy' kind of coordination as the horizontal mortiser, in fact. A good trick with valuable veneered boards is to pin hardwood lips all round the edges at exactly the same height as the veneer. They will protect the vulnerable edges from snagging or wearing right through. With a hand-held pad, never let it ride off the edges of the work, which will undoubtedly round over or 'dub'.

Most sliding-table belt sanders have a vertical fence above, and a flat surface under, the top run of the belt, where it's easiest and safest to do small pieces. Make sure the stop is in the right position to retain the work, which you should lay down gently but with a firm grip. When you're sure you can feel what sort of pull the belt is giving you to work against, you can push the timber down on the belt. Keep your fingers out of the belt's way! *Always* put the work hard up against the stop as you lay it on the belt (fig. 8.10). If you're lucky enough to have a machine with edge-sanding facilities then you must also make sure that the stops are set up right and the work properly held against them (fig. 8.11). The speed and power of these machines – the belts move at around 15m a second – makes it tempt-

Fig. 8.12: This particular combination drum/belt machine has a bevel-sanding facility. Set the angle carefully and test it

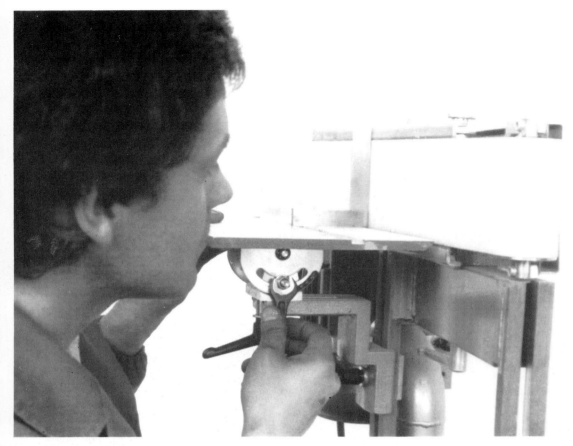

Fig. 8.13: Setting table and belt accurately with an engineer's square, the belt in the vertical position

ing to use coarse belts to take quite large lumps off small pieces, instead of using a plane or saw. Your own hand-pressure allows a fine touch. It doesn't mean don't be careful, though – it always pays to bear in mind that the only safe woodworking machine is one completely unconnected to any power, with no human in sight!

Disc sanding

Not the drill attachment, but an independent machine with a disc (anything up to 24in diameter) with a table and fence hard up to it. Like belts, discs of various sizes and grits are available; the smaller ones are extremely useful for

trimming endgrain and other small-section work that needs a lot taken off in a short time. But remember that even with the fine-grit discs, you won't get anything like a 'finish finish' – the circular path of the grit will inevitably show up on long grain, and even endgrain if it is close and hard. Always bear in mind that half the disc is travelling up, half of it down, *so put the work on the 'down' side without fail*. This means, of course, that the maximum area you can sand in one go is limited by the size of the disc – half its diameter, in fact. Jigs, stops and adjustable fences can be devised to get a variety of angles and bevels but if you are concerned only about getting exact right angles to a face or edge, you

Fig. 8.14: A high vertical fence is essential for accurate endgrain trimming; you can make your own

Fig. 8.15: A dust-mask is essential, even if you have extraction

must meticulously check the accuracy of your fence to the face of the disc. The combination drum/belt machine shown has a range of adjustments to the table for angle-sanding (fig. 8.12), a drum at one end for curved work (fig. 8.4), and on top of that the tables and drums move through 90°. Fig. 8.13 shows the belt vertical with the table horizontal, and an engineer's square being used to set it up accurately. The position is reversed in fig. 8.14, where the table's vertical height is used as a guide for accurate endgrain – sanding of a long stile. Adjustable table height will allow you to work on different parts of the belt on this sort of machine; don't turn it over to use the other half, you'll be running the belt the wrong way round. All the safety considerations apply with machines like this; remember to hold the work firmly, always use stops and fences, and watch the tips of your fingers!

Extraction

The large belt sanders, because of the speed of the belt, tend to carry a lot of the dust along the belt to where it's collected in one of the drum housings and taken away through a mobile or built-in extraction system (see Chapter 9). It's out of the question to use these machines without some form of dust control, for the sake of your own lungs, and also because accumulations of hot dust are potentially explosive. Wear a mask (fig. 8-15) if you'll be working on a belt sander for more than a minute or two; dust collection cannot by the very nature of the machine be particularly efficient. The smaller disc and belt sanders are even more difficult to extract, and perversely it's often on these machines that you want to take large lumps off small pieces – and make huge quantities of dust. The only answer is a good mask, and clothing tight at the wrists and neck.

CHAPTER 9

DUST EXTRACTION AND WASTE REMOVAL

Dust has been the woodworker's bane since the first meeting between steel and wood. Progress, in the form of machinery, has made us more efficient in producing chips and dust as well as saving time and energy in just about every woodworking operation. Long-term effects on health are very worrying, but difficult to gauge; however, every woodworker must be familiar with that blocked-up feeling after a day's sanding. Dust also creates a major safety issue in the

Fig. 9.1: No portable power tool is particularly easy to extract; orbital sanders certainly need it

workshop, as briefly explained in Chapter 1.

Dust, shavings and offcuts on the floor and around machines not only present an obstacle course, but can create a serious fire risk. Most workshop insurance policies require 'all shavings, sawdust and other refuse to be swept up daily and removed weekly'.

One of the greatest dangers is when chips fall on to the machine table. Any misjudgement in clearing them away with your hands can lead to an accident with revolving cutters or blades. The short answer, of course, is – don't use flesh, use wood to push bits and pieces away.

Power tools

Portable routers, planers, sanders, jigsaws and drills all produce dust which is very difficult to extract (fig. 9.1). Where large or continuous amounts of waste are being produced or vision is interfered with by flying particles, you should wear some form of mask and eye protection.

Fig. 9.2: Thicknessing without extraction causes thick dust, inconvenient and dangerous piles of shavings, and presents the possibility of the work bruising from chips

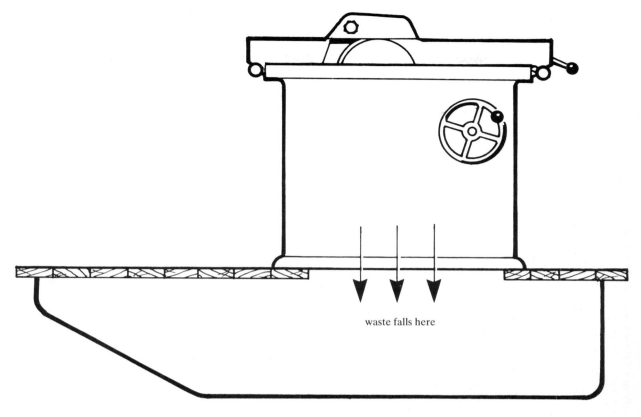

waste falls here

Fig. 9.3: A new approach to saw-pits for machines with an open base

Some manufacturers of portable power tools have been quick to realise the dust problem and have made planers and sanders with integral collection bags, jigsaws with built-in air jets that allow a clear view of the cutting line, and other additions; but the problem remains with many tools.

Free-standing machines

Planing machines are the worst offenders, producing large volumes of waste. Surfacing waste is deposited in the base of the machine, which when it isn't extracted can soon build up to a level where the revolving cutter-block picks up the chips and spits them out into the tables. For commercial use, of course, the Woodwork Machines Regulations 1974 require efficient ex-

traction on these and most other machines.

The better surfacing machines have a slope built in below the cutter-block, which allows the waste to fall away. Even so, regular clearance at floor level is necessary. Machines with cabinet bases that trap the waste and offer little access should be avoided if you don't have or aren't planning to have good extraction equipment. This problem is magnified on combined planer/thicknessers, because the thicknessing table (which in any case should be fully lowered) prevents the waste from clearing, making frequent stoppages necessary.

Thicknessing machines produce waste thick and fast, and in their bare form deposit heaps of chips on the floor in front of the machine, as well as a haze in the air (fig. 9.2). Prolonged use becomes very uncomfortable, not only for operators but anyone working nearby. With this type of machine the main objective is to prevent the dust becoming airborne by fitting hoods that deflect the waste downwards.

Machinery equipped with mechanical feeds (thicknessers, moulders, automatic lathes and so on) should be connected to an extractor, not only because of the large and continuous volume of waste, but also to prevent a build-up of chips in the machine itself. If feed rollers are not kept clear of loose chips, surface finish can be marred when they're pressed into the face of the work. With resinous woods such as pine, the problem is increased because the goo tends to get permanently stuck to the rollers, and frequent machine stops are inevitable to remove the build-up.

With circular saws, the main problem is again one of build-up of waste in the base of the machine. When the saw is used illegally (with crown guard and riving-knife removed) for

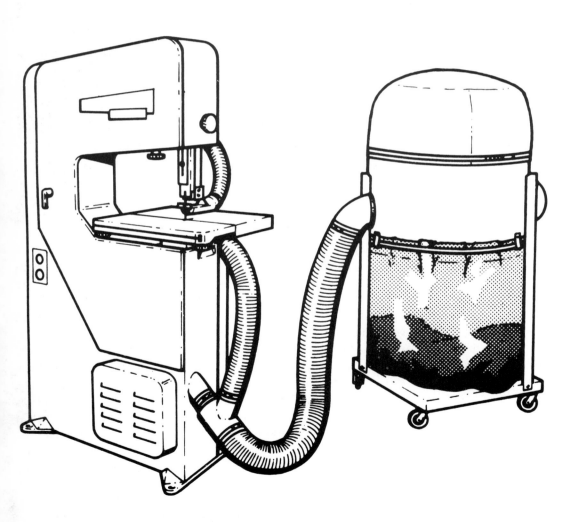

Fig. 9.5: Special duct-kits for a mobile extractor may be necessary if you do a lot of bandsawing

Fig. 9.6: If they're well made, home-made hoods can be extremely efficient – especially on planer/thicknessers

grooving, rebating, or tenoning, the machinist is exposed to a continuous stream of dust that is picked up by the revolving blade and thrown over head and shoulders. Fig. 9.3 shows an idea for overcoming the build-up inside machines.

As the spindle moulder is such an adaptable and variable machine, dust extraction is often minimal for much the same reasons as proper guarding also tends to be neglected – it's time-consuming to set up for a small amount of work. Extraction is essential for long runs of moulding, or permanent spindling set-ups. For straightforward moulding operations using the standard fences, it's easy to fit an extraction hood behind the fences (see Chapter 6), but with curved work where a ring fence, ball-bearing guide or similar set-up is in operation, 100% extraction can be difficult. Because of the way in which curved components are presented to the machine, the direction of the chips isn't always controllable. Hoods can be fitted, but they often interfere with the work.

The overhead router is similar to the spindle moulder in that the unpredictability of the flow of chips makes extraction difficult. There are combined extraction hoods and guards that overcome this (fig. 9.4), and with a certain amount of ingenuity you can make your own.

If you have a separate tenoning machine, it's likely that you're in a workshop that puts a large volume of work through it, and extraction is already there. Tenoning removes a large amount of waste material, so permanent connection to an extractor is essential if constant stoppages for clearances are to be avoided.

Dust does not present a great problem with bandsaws, except with continuous use or deep cutting. The main problem is that dust tends to be carried round by the blade and deposited over the machine table, work and operator. Brushes are fitted to the bigger machines to prevent this: fig. 9.5 shows an efficient bandsaw extraction system.

Sanding machines produce probably the most offensive, and also highly combustible, dust. Most manufacturers of mobile cyclone-type extraction units advise against using their products with sanding machines. Belt, drum, bobbin, disc sanding and linishing machines should be 'plumbed' into a separate ducting system employing spark arresters, high efficiency filters, and a cabinet collector that offers some protec-

tion against explosion. Even this is not enough when toxic fumes are also present – in this case, take expert advice.

Machines like chisel mortisers and pillar drills aren't generally worth connection to an extractor. Here the problem is not one of volume of waste, but its inevitable obstruction of pencil lines or centres on the work piece. A constant or controllable jet of compressed air is an efficient method of clearance, and even hooking up a good vacuum-cleaner on 'blow' over the work is worth doing.

Hoods

Until fairly recently dust extraction as we know it today was a mere dream – so on older, used or reconditioned machines, there will almost cer-

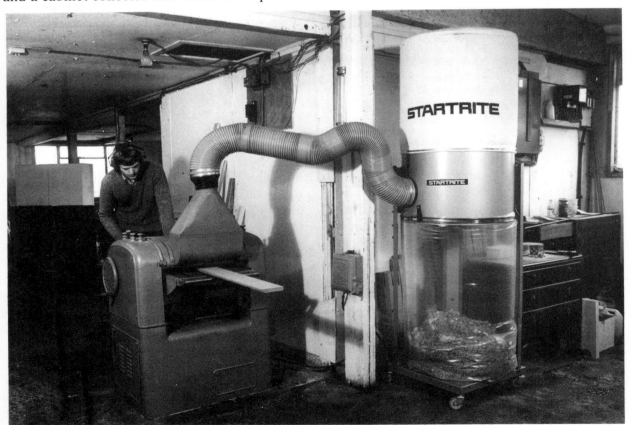

Fig. 9.7: A mobile extractor connected to a planer/thicknesser. Compare the effect with fig. 9.2!

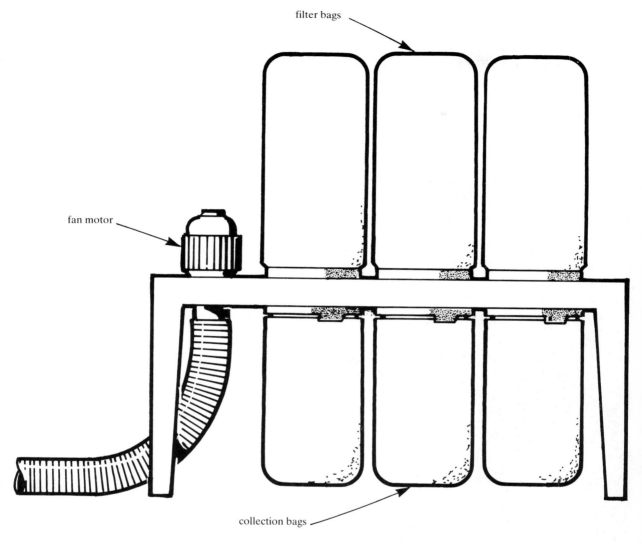

Fig. 9.8: A multi-bag 'mobile' unit can also be a good base for a built-in duct system

tainly be no obvious means of extractor connection.

Most dust extraction engineers are able to fabricate one-off hoods, ducting, or even design combined hoods and guarding. For many machines though, it should be possible for the resourceful woodworker to construct simple hoods from stout plywood (fig. 9.6). The main requirement is the smooth passage of waste. Hoods should be positioned in line with the main stream of chips so their initial momentum assists the extraction process, and be as close to the blade or cutter as practicable.

Hoods fitted over cutter-blocks should be securely fixed in place and not allowed to rattle round. Some form of ventilation may also be necessary, as noise levels can be increased by badly designed or constructed hoods which become a sort of trumpet.

Extraction hoods often also guard the unused or exposed parts of blades or cutters. When designing or constructing such fittings, you must

Mobile extractors

For the majority of small or medium-sized work-shops, where the thicknesser is the main offender and other machines only present an occasional problem, the popular mobile single-bag unit is the obvious choice (fig. 9.7). Mobile extractors are available in all sorts of shapes, sizes and wattages. Although there are exceptions, the mobile single-bag unit is only really capable (at its best) of handling one machine at a time.

Not only are mobile units idea for all machinery as and when the need arises, they can also be fitted with various attachments that turn them into giant vacuum cleaners for the once-a-year workshop spring-clean. They work on the cyclone principle – waste material is drawn into the unit by the fan, where the heavier wood particles are separated from the air and fall into the collection bag. The air then returns to the workshop through the linen filter.

Machine-planing and sawing often mix larger pieces of waste with the usual sawdust (when planing wild boards, for example, an explosion inside the machine reveals troublesome grain or a loose knot). Although most extractors can cope with pieces of this size, they aren't really suited to handling 'solids'. Rags and large pieces of paper should also be avoided, as the motor could overheat if they get into the fan.

Fig. 9.9: 'Dustbin' wood waste heaters are simple in concept: with a bit of ingenuity you can make your own

consider the possibilities of flying cutters, and use material strong enough to retain them.

Industrial regulations concerning dust extraction largely revolve round the length of time that individual machines are at work. For those who come under the jurisdiction of the Health and Safety Executive, a copy of *The Woodworking Machines Regulations 1974* makes a worthwhile read.

What to look for

The power of any extractor must be considered first. Power is usually rated in cubic feet per minute (cfm), or its metric equivalent. Different manufacturers have their own ideas and opinions on power, but as examples, the average circular saw, small spindle moulder or 10-12in planer will require around 550 cfm, and 18in planers or tenoning machines around 750 cfm.

The size of ducting will usually be dictated by the inlet diameter on the extractor unit, and should be in proportion to the power of the motor, but again the average 12in saw or planer needs 5in, and 19in planers need 6in-diameter ducting. Obviously, when considering the power of a given extraction unit, a lot depends on the type of work your machines do. Although you may only ever feed narrow strips through your 30in thicknesser, it's wise to cover its maximum capability. If your unit is some distance from the machinery it will serve, or a branch is to be fitted, then some power drop will be inevitable and power must be increased proportionally.

The capacity of the collection bag or bags on multiple machines is also important. Although a one-bag unit may well have adequate power to handle the output of a large planing machine, if it's continuously running at anything near its maximum capacity, stoppages for bag changing will be so frequent that a multi-bag unit would make much more sense (fig. 9.8).

A system

The next step up is permanent ducting to each individual machine feeding a central extraction unit, often housed outside the main building. Although not outside the scope of the resourceful woodworker, this really requires the services of an extraction specialist. Permanent extraction systems demand a large, and (you hope!) one-off investment, so it is essential that you take every consideration into account. Most extraction engineers offer a complete planning and technical service, and are able to solve most dust problems.

The power needed for permanent extraction systems is dictated by the number and size of machines, the distance from each machine to the point of collection, and the number of branches or junctions. In most small workshops, machines (although often running together) are not often cutting at their full power, so the size of motor, and therefore cost, can be kept down by the fitting of dampers in the system that direct the air-flow to come only from the machines actually producing waste.

A useful addition when planning an extraction system is the fitting of a sweep-up point. This is a duct opening at floor level where workshop sweepings can be directed.

The majority of extractors use medium gauge see-through polythene collection bags, which can usually be obtained from the manufacturer or supplier of the unit. There are alternatives – for storage and reusability, heavy gauge polythene bags are ideal, although expensive. If you dump your waste and don't want the inconvenience or discomfort of emptying lots of bags of sawdust, then rolls of light-gauge polythene tubing of the right circumference for your machine can be used. This is cut off and knotted at one end to seal it for use.

Some extractors are of a size that allows you to use an average refuse sack, but these are

Fig. 9.10: A free-standing wood waste burner can produce enough heat for quite large spaces. They will take large offcuts as well as dust and even coke or coal

really no cheaper than other ones generally available, and you can't see the sawdust level. It may be worth getting a quote from a specialist supplier if you are buying more than a few hundred bags each time.

When choosing a mobile extractor or built-in collection unit, check the way in which the collection bags are held in place. On some units the arrangements are very poor, both in quality and design of fasteners, and ease of operation. Over a long period, quick and easy bag changing will be much appreciated.

Using wood waste

When the next piece of mahogany passes through the planer and the dust disappears up the pipe, the story should be far from over. Not

Fig. 9.11: A briquetter – quite an investment, but worth looking at the onward profit if you produce enough waste

only are there ways to save money from using wood waste; in some cases a handsome profit can be made.

What you do with your wood waste largely depends upon the volume. Small and inconsistent quantities may have to be dumped, and you may even have to pay for their removal. On the other hand, large and regular producers of wood waste (especially softwood shavings) may well be able to sell it to specialist companies. Offcuts can easily be sold or given away as firewood.

The obvious choice for most workshops is to use wood waste for winter-time heat. However, do check that your insurance allows this. The type of sawdust that most woodworkers produce will usually be dry and therefore a valuable fuel. Wet wood waste, such as that produced by sawmills, can also be burnt, but has a lower heat value – it may be necessary to mix wet and dry to allow it to burn. However, a very cold December can soon erode your summertime stock. There are in fact many wood users (sawmills, joinery shops) who are only too glad to get rid of the stuff. Transporting it can be another matter, as it doesn't take many bags of sawdust to fill the average car boot or van. If you have to make lots of trips, the petrol costs can easily cancel out your fuel savings.

Wood waste heaters

One of the most popular small workshop sawdust burners is the 'dustbin' type (fig. 9.9), which generates heat by slow combustion of the fuel material packed inside. Output can be regulated by simple adjustment of the air vents to give a comfortable working temperature. It also cooks some of the best toasted sandwiches you ever tasted!

In larger workshops wood waste heaters can be either free-standing self-contained units, just requiring a flue connection (fig. 9.10), or they can be housed outside the main workshop area with heat delivered by ducting.

Heating output is rated in BTUs. Your requirements can be roughly calculated by multiplying workshop volume (cubic feet) by five; thus a 1000sq ft workshop, with a ceiling height of 10ft, requires a heater rated at 50,000BTUs. Obviously, efficiency depends to a large degree on the type and construction of the building and its level of insulation.

This type of unit will not only burn the usual offcuts, sawdust and shavings, but also straw, paper and any other combustible material. They usually burn solid fuel (coal and coke) as back-up alternatives. Stoking can be done manually or by an automatic fuel-delivery line (usually fed by a manually filled hopper). Connecting this to the extraction system proper offers total automation. For those working in smokeless zones, afterburners can be fitted to comply with the requirements of the Clean Air Act. During warm weather, hot air can be 'dumped' or used for timber drying.

Whatever system you choose to suit your individual needs, the saving on oil, gas or electric heating usually means that the initial investment is easily recovered over a very short period (within 12 months in some cases), resulting in almost-free heat for ever after.

Briquetting

If you have many machines at work all day, a briquette press (fig. 9.11) may be the answer to your waste problem. Although requiring a high initial investment, it could create a profitable offshoot of the main business. There are machines now which pulverise all your waste to a consistent particle size, for another installation to turn them into briquettes. You can get the two for a total of about £5000 upwards – a significant cost for the small workshop, remembering that you have also invested time and/or money in a business. But you can sell the briquettes, bagged up in builder's materials sacks, for £2-£3 a bag: it won't take long at that rate for the machines to become a profit centre on their own. You do need to be creating that waste, though.

INDEX

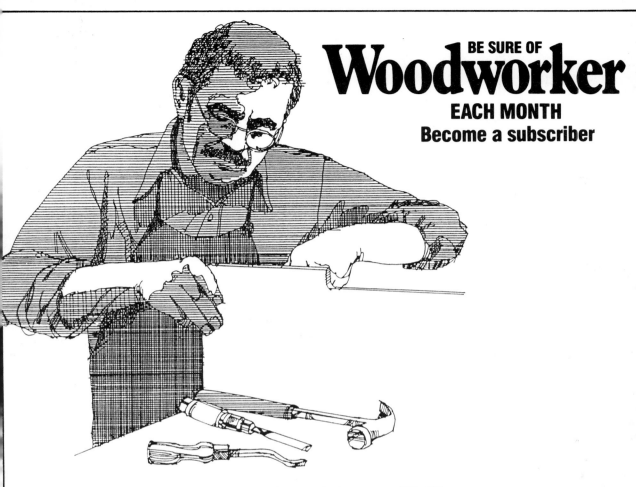